To Ed,

Hope

these stories from

a different time

The Lie
of the
Land

Best wishes

P

Feb 2014

The Lie
of the
Land

PJ Cunningham

Ballpoint Press

*To my mother Mary Jo, my father Frank,
my Aunt Sheila and Uncle John,
whose footprints are etched
across every page of this book.*

Published in 2013 by Ballpoint Press
4 Wyndham Park, Bray, Co Wicklow, Republic of Ireland.
Telephone: 00353 86 821 7631
Email: ballpointpress1@gmail.com
Web: www.ballpointpress.ie

ISBN 978-0-9572072-7-1

Book design and production by Elly Design

Printed and bound by GraphyCems

Contents

About the Author

PJ CUNNINGHAM is a journalist and publisher who was brought up on a small farm in Clara, Co Offaly but now lives in Bray, Co Wicklow.

His previous book of short stories, A. N. Other, centred on rural life as seen through GAA activity and was published in 2001.

He is married to Rosemary O'Grady and has five children.

Preface

THIS collection of stories strays between the more structured short story genre and simple recollections of old tales.

The truth is all eighteen stories are both – and neither.

Originally, I had planned to write a series of stories capturing both the innocence and cruelty that surrounds animal life growing up on a farm.

As I quarried further into my memory bank, I disturbed a vault of hidden subjects which had more to do with people and relationships than animals.

I found I had at best only a disjointed image of how my ancestors worked, lived and interacted with those around them.

Of course I had my own experiences and observations but beyond that I had to use information that was handed down to imagine a bigger and hopefully more accurate picture of the lie of the land as it affected our extended family.

In the end it became a very cathartic exercise and I now truly feel I understand the people I've written about much more than I ever could if I had not undertaken this project.

My hope is that you will relate to some or all of these stories and find the reading experience more rewarding as a result.

1

The Rabbit
And The
Weasel

THE rabbit was running and squealing and most unusually heading in our direction instead of scarpering at the sight of a human.

I was five years old and I did not understand what was going on. The men helping my father in the field, Charlie and Cathal, looked around at where the noise came from and watched intently. My father, his brown waistcoat unbuttoned to allow air around his body, touched the red neckerchief he had put on earlier when he felt the sun burning up the back of his neck.

His eyes darted to where the rabbit was and then a look of bewilderment came across his face.

The rabbit was big and brown and had gone against the instinct of a species by taking refuge with the enemy.

"Look, it's because of the weasel," my father said as he threw his two-grained fork into the ground and headed towards the clearly distraught animal.

The sense of danger and the look of the rabbit did something to normal time in my head and it seemed to me that I was watching this little episode in our hayfield in slow motion.

My father went towards the rabbit as if it was a child; he made a soothing sound through his closed mouth as if to say to the little frightened creature that it was with friends. Astonishingly, the rabbit kept running towards him and my father swept it up in his big strong and safe arms.

"Okay, okay, shshshssh. He can't get you now," he said soothingly while gently shaking his arms up and down in rhythmic fashion.

The rabbit was visibly trembling and my father brushed its coat all the way down the back of its ears through to the tail and back again, all the while talking to the frightened animal as if it was a child.

Charlie, a small sinewy man with balding grey hair, a red face and a Woodbine butt in the corner of his mouth, leaned on the handle of the fork and pointing at the weasel declared: "Look at him. Look at him over there, the way he is watching."

"There are no weasels in Ireland, only stoats," declared his nephew, as he swept at the rows of hay with his two-grained fork in a tidy and economical use of his wrists.

He wiped away the sweat from his brow and flicked the Players cigarette butt he had in his mouth into a nearby ditch close to where the pony was tied in shelter from the direct rays of the sun.

I loved animals and particularly rabbits; they were timid but gentle and I was hoping that maybe we could bring this one home and mind it in the house. In fact, I was excited at the thought that this might happen.

Just then my mother arrived with the tea and freshly baked currant bread she had made specially for the men working in the field at the hay.

She brought the tea in a three-quart can that normally was used to deliver milk to the neighbours. In her wickerwork basket on the front of the bike she had a bottle of milk, sugar and butter rolled up in a dishcloth to keep it as cool as possible on the journey down from the house. She walked her bicycle through the field using the basket to carry the food and drink.

Having laid out the food on a torn hessian bag on the ground and poured out the mugs of tea as if we were about to go on a picnic, she called out to the men that the grub was ready.

Looking across as we made our way towards her, her eyes lit up with surprise when she saw my father arriving with a rabbit in his arms.

"In the name of God, where did you get that?" she asked with a tone of incredulity in her voice.

Charlie once again drew our attention to the weasel/stoat which was keeping a vigil on proceedings while maintaining a healthy distance between himself and our gathering.

"Well, he's latched onto that little furry fellow for sure," said Charlie as he pointed to the hunter. "We could bring that poor rabbit to Timbuktu but your man over there will follow us every step of the way."

My mother seemed bemused by what she was hearing. I, too, was listening to the adults talk but didn't really know what they meant about going away to wherever that funnily-named place was.

"It's true," my father said grimly as he looked down on the frail animal in his grasp. "This poor thing's number is up if we let it go back into the wild."

"Well, we can't keep it at home," said my mother, mindful that we had dogs and cats around the yard who would tear it asunder at the first opportunity.

My father again looked down at the rabbit and a brief cloud of sadness crossed his face as he did so.

We were all eating mother's hot cake and tea and his was going cold in front of him.

My mother stretched her hands out to take the rabbit and told my father to wipe himself down and eat up before the food was spoilt.

She took over the minding of the rabbit and also began hushing the creature as if it was a baby; she shook it gently in her arms as if she was trying to get it to nod off to sleep. As she did so, she walked away from us down toward where she had parked her bicycle underneath a hedgerow which had a number of overhanging branches.

The weasel/stoat readjusted his position to keep my mother and his quarry in his sights, edging a little closer to observe what they were doing in the cool shade provided by the tree.

My father chewed thoughtfully on his bread but appeared fascinated by how nature was playing out a game of hunter and prey under our noses.

"Terrifying. He's terrifying the rabbit the way he keeps his eyes locked on him," he said to Charlie.

I don't remember how events occurred in real time after that. It was the disjointed bits of information which were spoken from time to time which helped me surmise what must have happened.

I heard a sound from where my mother was standing with her back to us and half hidden by the foliage of the branches which were weighed down towards the ground. I remember moments later having my attention drawn to the weasel/stoat as it appeared to check out what was going on with his rabbit. Having watched intently for half a minute or so, he then turned and went away, looking back every few yards to confirm what his instinct had told him.

Charlie was about to say something but my father put his hand up to his lips and made some hand signs which didn't make any sense to me.

A while later, my mother came back empty-handed, nodded knowingly to my father and the men, who all acknowledged her message dutifully as they stood up from the makeshift picnic setting to find their forks before returning to pike the hay.

Seeing my face and the sense of shock that was growing through it, my mother caught me gently by the hand, saying that we would walk down to Maggie's shop and buy an ice-cream.

"You're a great little trooper helping your father here all day and the least we can do is buy you a treat."

When I asked her about the rabbit and where it was, she squeezed my hand a little more firmly than before and said with a far-off tone to her voice: "The little rabbit is safe from that dirty weasel now. Don't you worry your little head, the poor defenceless animal is safe as houses."

2

Rosary
Time

THE pips for the news at 10 on Radio Eireann were the reminder to get ready for the nightly kneeling marathon that was our family's Rosary. Most houses got a blast of the five glorious, joyful or sorrowful mysteries out of the way with only the Hail Holy Queen at the end... and that was that.

But the Rosary was only warming up at that stage in our kitchen. We still had to face up to 10 trimmings – extra prayers for special intentions.

My father would begin these 'afters' with – Three Hail Marys for Matt Talbot (about whom we had heard a lot), Fr Willie Doyle (about whom we had heard very little) and the conversion of Russia (which he, my father that is, seemed to be on a one-man crusade to achieve).

How could you follow such noble sentiments in one kneeling? But follow it my mother did.

She came up with more banal but worthy recipients of our prayers. "Three Hail Marys for the homeless, the Travellers on the side of the road and, in particular, for the sailors on stormy seas that night."

My father was now due back in, storming the pearly gates again... and his second lot was subject to seasonal adjustments.

Three Hail Marys that the weather would take up for the haymaking or the barley cutting.

Or conversely it might be Three Hail Marys that the fine weather would break before every blessed blade of grazing grass was all burnt in the Church Field.

Back to my mother – Three Hail Marys for the souls in purgatory, for those recently departed and the gift of a happy death.

On and on it went. My father – Three Hail Marys that there would no reactors in the cattle test for TB that year.

There we were trading prayer to shivering prayer until... Thirty Hail Marys later – on top of those five decades of the Rosary – we staggered gingerly back to our feet, happy in the knowledge that we had more than done our bit to save the world for at least another 24 hours.

My cousins up the road though had a much more pragmatic approach to the Rosary – they seldom if ever said it. Or at least not religiously, like us.

In pre or early television times of rural Ireland in the early to mid-sixties, it was still commonplace for people to ramble in to a house up to nine or ten o'clock at night either for a chat or in the case of this particular visitor – to get something to eat.

Billy was a Protestant bachelor living near my aunt's farm and with no woman to look after him at home, he developed a habit of making calls on all the neighbours on a sort of rota basis.

If he got food in one place, he would go back night after night until that particular neighbour got fed up and "ran" him by pretending they were all just on their way to bed.

Now my aunt, bless her, wouldn't hurt the poor soul with such a crude approach. Indeed, on the first visit or two, she would pump Billy for all the information she could get... And enjoy finding out how many of the neighbour's cattle across the fields had gone down in the test...

Or which of the red-headed Murphy girls got engaged to the big farmer from the other side of the parish.

At this stage there was some sort of a fair trade – Billy's information for my aunt's Spotted Dick cake – piping hot and just out of the oven, covered in melted butter and a big mug of tae to wash it all down.

By the second or third night however, her charity would begin to wear thin and she would be preoccupied the next day as she hatched a plan to put a stop to the nightly visitations.

That night once she heard the gate opening in the lower yard, she knew she had about 10 seconds in which to ready her troops before Billy's arrival.

"Quick, quick, everyone," she would order in the loudest whisper imaginable... "down on your knees."

THE LIE OF THE LAND

We obeyed like a chorus line in a musical.

Then just as Billy lifted the latch and opened the door into the kitchen, he would be met by my aunt's poker face opposite him piously proclaiming – "Thou, oh Lord, will open my lips," to which we would, even more piously answer: "And my tongue shall announce thy praise..."

Eyes almost outside his head trying to make sense of what he was witnessing, Billy would scan the room only to see Rosary beads dangling in front of him as we all knelt over the wooden chairs facing the Sacred Heart picture. It left him as a good, God-fearing Protestant with no option but to turn on his heel and disappear into the darkness.

Shushing down our sniggers at the success of her strategy, my aunt would continue, mar dhea, praying in a loud voice – "The first sorrowful mystery... the prayer and agony in the garden."

We would mumble a few more pretend prayers until she was happy Billy was finally out of earshot and well on his way to a neighbour's door at the top of the road.

Then she would rise off her knees, bless herself... Father, Son and Holy Ghost, Aw-mennnnn... and say with a chuckle: "I don't know who're the biggest Protestants – poor Billy or us after the mockery we've made of the Rosary this night."

3

The German Neighbour

CONSIDERING that very few people where I grew up travelled more than seven miles to the nearest biggest town, it was slightly exotic for us to have a German as a neighbouring farmer near the lands we knew as The Sally Gardens.

This farm was bought by him following the government's relaxation on allowing foreigners to come in and buy up land in the country. He used to come over only once or twice a year as he had hired an auctioneer from another county to act as a 'herd' for the livestock which grazed on the farm.

But no matter what way you looked at it, that was never going to work in the same way as if it was an owner looking after his own cattle. The auctioneer was a decent and affable man but in the course of his daily and weekly chores, herding the German's cattle and tending to the fences etc was hardly top of his priority list.

My father knew the man from before, having met him at local fairs and land lettings down the years; they would talk over the fence between our mearings the odd time they bumped into each other while checking on the stock.

Invariably Mickey, the auctioneer, would end his conversation by saying that he'd appreciate it if my dad threw an eye across the boundaries on the days he (Mickey) would be unable to travel the 10 or so miles from where he lived.

During supper in the kitchen on such evenings, my mother would quiz my father on who he had met during the day. When he told her of his encounter with Mickey and how he had asked if we could keep an eye on the German's cattle, she bridled with indignation.

"Isn't it a great world all the same," she said. "There's the German paying your man a fistful of money to act as his herd and he wants you to do the job for him. Did he offer you any money for it?" she asked rhetorically.

"You can bet your bottom dollar he didn't. He must think we're all right eejits around here."

My father didn't like criticism where he was cast by my mother in the role of a simpleton but on this occasion he was happy enough to respond matter-of-factly: "I told him that more often than not his cattle grazed and sheltered up the other side of the farm, so I wouldn't be that good to him on a day-to-day basis."

The was because the German's acreage was quite boggy down beside us but the contours of the land rose as you went away from our boundaries which provided better grass for the cattle.

I checked on that for a number of days afterwards and sure enough what my father told my mother was perfectly true – the German's cattle were nearly always away from our side of the holding.

The summertime had its way of bringing its own share of drama around farms. For instance the road which serviced both ours and the German's farm was normally very quiet. That made it an ideal setting for Travellers who congregated there every year from the West of Ireland with their camps, horses, dogs, horse-drawn caravans and business tent. While there, they made pots, pans and buckets which they sold to the houses and farms nearby.

Obviously with such an influx of population, there was increased use by the travelling people of the fields for myriad reasons – as toilets, as areas where they could walk and in the case of their children, where they could allow them to play without fear.

There was a tremendous understanding between the settled people and those who came in this fashion every year. My father would allow them to bring their horses through our fields to drink at the Little River and would also point out to them what timber they could cut for their fires if they wanted to take wood out of our ditches.

It was by no means a one-way street as the Travellers would hand him a big enamel bucket gratis as their payback or sometimes if he was down on his own – most of our land was a mile away from the farmhouse – they would call him over and give him a cup of tea and a slice of bread dripping with gooseberry jam they made from the wild fruit picked in the ditches.

If truth be told their presence in the area, particularly as we lived so far away, was a source of worry to my dad. The young Travellers had long hours to kill every fine summer's day and were forever either leaving gates open in fields or breaking down fences – which meant that cattle were not as secure as they could or should be.

"What can we do. They are as entitled as anyone to camp there," he would say, adding: "They were run off the land during the famine and the least we can do is give them the use of it back for the few months they are around."

My mother agreed but only to a certain extent. She would give my father the odd cake of homemade bread to pass on to the women down there but believed that my father was too soft when it came to warning them about going in and out of our fields.

As always she had a point and it was made very forcibly to us when one of our younger heifers went missing. We searched high up and low down along the river, the ditches and in the furze which grew across the upper third of the Sally Gardens – but there was no trace of the beast.

Losing an animal at any time of the year represented a crisis. In this instance my father would have budgeted for her sale that autumn to the butcher as part of the input of money he needed to pay the bills. As we were out of school and our cousins were as well, we were rounded up to check the German's farm on a forensic basis – literally a yard-by-yard search of the holding.

It brought us to places which we had never been before – across by the Canon Lambe's, a retired Church of Ireland minister, who I never spoke to on a one-to-one basis in my lifetime.

The search was like a game for us, at once exciting with a daring to see if we could find what we were looking for. I would have enjoyed it much more except my father's expression grew into one of increasing agitation as the hours went by, meaning this was about real life and not child's play.

When the search brought us back towards our own land, one of the young Traveller lads whistled to us out of a tree he had climbed beside their caravan on the road fence.

"Mister, what are you looking for?" he asked in my father's direction.

"A heifer that's gone missing," he replied.

The young lad slid down the tree in the twinkle of an eye and bounded over the ditch as if he was on springs.

He was breathless by the time he reached us. "Is it a bull, mister? Because I seen one up in a boghole at the back of the hill over there," he explained as he pointed along our mearing line with the German's some hundreds of yards away.

"That's probably ours," Daddy said, notwithstanding the fact that he was talking female (heifer) and the youngster was talking about a male animal (bull).

"I brang the greyhound out for a walk, sir, early this

morning. I was giving it a run over there when it stopped all of a sudden and began sniffing. There was a little gulley down from the field into the bog where there was fresh grass and I'd say the bull went after that before sinking in the boghole."

I was amazed at how knowledgeable the Traveller appeared to be on why an animal might risk safety for new grass but for sure that was a genuine lure for an animal and a danger for such a farmer as my father.

Without realising it, I spent a lot of my time trying to judge the mood of a situation by scanning his face. This time it had a fatalistic look on it – he already had assessed that we had lost an animal – a big setback on the earnings from a small holding.

The boy led us out at a good pace up to where he had seen the animal and himself and my father were running fast as they arrived at the narrowing into the gulley.

"Quick," my father said back to us, "the animal is alive." We all felt a sense of relief that our expedition might have a happy ending.

However the joy in his voice changed almost immediately when his vision adjusted to the animal in the darkness of the sunken gulley.

"It's... it's one of the German's," he said, "but you're right young fella, it is indeed a young bull," he agreed, as he patted the young lad on the back as a sign of approval.

Although strictly speaking farmers were supposed to castrate their bull calves at a young age, sometimes the animals grew and put on weight quicker if they were allowed to keep their manhood for a little longer. In the case of the German, we later learned that this was a purebred specimen with official papers. It was being held to run with some heifers which he had at another farm in Westmeath.

At that moment, though, the young bull appeared totally spent from trying to get out of the mire. By the time we arrived he was virtual deadwood, wedged into the boghole as it sucked most of his bulk down under its surface.

I was sent back to the pony's cart by my father, told to take the reins out of her winkers and to bring back the spade with me. While I was gone, he got the rest of the lads to pull tufts of grass and rushes and have them ready to give the young bull a lift if we could get him to lunge forward onto that makeshift pathway.

When I returned, my father dug a channel to drain some of the water away, then got down alongside the bull into the boghole and put a rope under his foremost legs to see if we could help to lift him up.

He told me to use the spade to slap the bull's back when he beckoned to me. That was the signal for my brother on one side and the young Traveller and our cousins on the other, to pull with all their might in the hope that it would help lift the bull to safety.

When the animal saw that he had a chance of escaping the earth's drag with this strategy, he renewed his effort to get out. On the signal I had slapped him on his back. Immediately he jumped with the fright and landed onto the sides of the grass and rushes-bed which had been lain down for him. The others encouraged him by shouting as if he was in a race to a finish line in a cycling event.

As he reached safety by jumping clear of the boghole, our gaze was distracted by the sight of seeing our heifer's head and front body part pop up from its submerged state at the top of the boghole.

At the time I thought the German's bull had drowned our little heifer but my father would only say what happened had been an accident of nature and overall, that it was good to save one of the animals. He explained that it was better to know where our own animal was even if it was dead than to be left wondering what had happened.

Back then, even when it was only animals that were involved, sex was a taboo subject. Ireland of the sixties wrapped its information tightly in little nods and glances but as time went by, I was old enough to understand what probably had happened.

Our young heifer must have come 'round', which was the local way of saying she came into heat for reproduction purposes. In such situations, young females will run through fencing or jump over ditches, particularly if there is a male nearby.

Similarly the male will seek out the female to service her as nature intended. The heifer almost certainly ran in the direction of the German's land acting as a tease to the bull, who followed her until she was cornered near the gulley. Thereafter it probably was a case of the male endeavouring to mate and driving the unfortunate heifer into the boghole and drowning her under his own weight.

That evening Mickey, the auctioneer, arrived at our house to thank my father for saving the animal from certain death.

"I saw the state of the young bull when I was herding and that young tinker lad told me you and the gosons pulled him to safety. And he also told me about your own heifer being lost..." he said as he gazed off into the distance.

He looked genuinely sorry and as they parted, my father thanked him for calling.

It was one of the few times though in my memory that a visitor walked out our front door without being offered a cup of tea. My mother just couldn't bring herself to do it.

"The cheek of him to come thanking us and the loss we're after suffering while his money is safe from the German because we looked out for him," she said with more than a little anger in her voice.

"You're right," my father agreed, "but the loss of the heifer wasn't his fault at the end of the day, was it?"

My mother threw her eyes up to the heavens wondering if she was living with a male version of Pollyanna as she put down the kettle to make the tea for us with her recently baked spotted dick.

Life went on as it always did... and a few weeks later a very officious package arrived with the postman addressed to my father. It was a lovely morning and we were in the kitchen for the breakfast after the milking.

We all sat around the table and my mother sat back down and used the breadknife to open up the very impressive looking 12 inch square orange envelope.

The package had come from the German. In the letter to my father, he explained how Mickey, the auctioneer, had given him a full account of how we had saved his bull while losing our own heifer. He thanked us profusely for our efforts and said Mickey had suggested that he should do something to show his gratitude.

He said he was enclosing a cheque for ten pounds for my father, some German sweets for the children who had helped to save the animal and he would see to it that Mickey delivered the first heifer calf from the progeny of the young bull whenever she was born on the other farm the following year.

We all listened attentively as my mother read out the letter in that gorgeous school-mistress sounding voice of hers that was faultless in its delivery. When she had finished my father smiled and said, as he often did at such moments: "That beats Banagher."

"Well, glory be to God," declared my mother. "And to think I insulted Mickey by not offering him a cup of tea. Lord, I can never look the man in the eye again."

4

A Pig In The Poke

NATURE has a wonderful way of working in the wild and on farms as well but from time to time something happens in its great cycle of birth and death which necessitates human intervention.

Enter Larry, which was one of triplet lambs born late in the season when others were virtually reared. My father ran the ram with the ewes to have it that they would lamb from mid-January on but in this case, it seems the ram didn't get this side of the business done in time, which meant we had triplets born around Easter.

To make matters worse, the particular ewe appeared to take an instant dislike to little Larry, not allowing him to feed on her milk, preferring the bigger two which we called Beau and Felix.

In her world, she must have seen that those two were stronger and more likely to survive so perhaps she was only following the instinct which had been handed down in her DNA for generations.

Hence the human intervention – my father saw that if he didn't get involved, Larry would become so weak that he would not survive. So he made the decision to bring the third lamb into the house, allowing him to 'live' in the big tea-chest on the far side of the fireplace where we fed him regularly from a teat and bottle as if he was a human baby.

Larry was a very affectionate lamb and his little black face lit up every time he saw us coming with his milk. We all loved him, my mother, my brother and I were forever picking him up and nursing him on our lap as he fed.

My father was more pragmatic and said we were spoiling the dumb animal to the extent that he would never be able to fend for himself when we put him back out on the farm with the other animals.

Around the same time as we were rearing Larry indoors, the sow had a litter and the runt (the smallest and weakest piglet) also had to be brought in and hand fed. We sought out another tea-chest box from Carey's grocery shop for him and because he was noisier, we put him in what we called 'The Little Room' behind the kitchen, which within a short time became known as 'The Pig's Room'.

My uncle 'christened' the piggy Pipsqueak, the name loosely based on a character in Dickens' book Great Expectations. My brother called the lamb Larry; my mother laughingly called them 'The Twins' and then we reduced the piglet's name to Pip.

They formed a liaison as they grew up in the yard and garden and as the weeks turned into months, Pip the piglet and Larry the lamb became inseparable brothers. Indeed 'twins' was a very apt description of the pair.

In early summer when the grass had grown out the back, the three late lambs and the piglets were allowed out for a few hours every day to eat on the free range. Pip and Larry both gravitated towards the other piglets without ever congregating around the ewe or the two late lambs which still were not integrated with the other sheep down in the lower fields we called The Bottoms, but would soon be allowed run with them.

The first dilemma came when that day finally arrived; the lambs no longer needed their mother's milk to survive and Larry had grown to be a strapping fellow thanks to the in-house spoiling he got from us.

My father wanted to send the three lambs down together with the ewe, arguing that the time had come for Larry to integrate back with his own kind.

It was easier said than done. When we brought them down on the pony and cart, the ewe and the other two lambs ran over to the rest almost immediately while Larry doubled back as my father and I locked up the back creel on the cart waiting to go home with us. We left the field, closed the gate behind us and drove down the road a small way before pulling in. We stole back quietly to see if he had gone down to the others; he hadn't and as soon as he either smelled or caught sight of us, bleated at us to take him home.

I was in favour of doing that there and then but my father said if we gave in once we'd never get him to stay down there. My mother was far from happy with that decision and said it was unfair on the poor orphan of a lamb to be left alone again, as it would remind him of the time his mother disowned him.

I was distraught and began to cry and when I let the pigs out to the garden I noticed that Pip was staying close to me as if he was trying to find out where Larry had disappeared to.

The happiest sounds I remember of my childhood was that evening when my uncle called in and my mother made him drive her down to The Bottoms in his car where she found Larry still waiting at the gate. She brought him home in the back seat of his Morris Minor. Immediately she put him out the back with Pip and the bleat and grunt of the pair as they were reunited is something that I've never forgotten. Two different animals, speaking two different languages, but the message was unmistakable – they were relieved and overjoyed to be together again.

Twins!

My father was cross about what had happened when he got home from working on our land in Woodfield but my mother refused to give way. Even animals were entitled to their version of happiness, she said; adding that: "The boys and me are happier too to have it this way."

My father looked at her, pulled an expression as if to say "have it your way" and then put his cap backwards on his head as he picked up the buckets on his way to milking in the cowshed.

"Maybe you're right, " he said to my mother sounding a bit sarcastic. "Let them enjoy the summer out there together, but I hope you have a story ready for the boys when the butcher comes with his cheque book in September."

5

The Clocking Hen

EVERY Irish household, at sometime or other, has a family feud hidden in their cupboard. Our family was no exception.

The falling-out was on my mother's side of the family and came a generation before any of us appeared on this planet. Back then such feuds were invariably fuelled by one of two things – land or money. In our case it was money.

Two sons of the house were both recently married and their ageing mother was known to have stashed a nice wad of money which she intended to hand over to both on an even split to help them pay for their new lives ahead as family men.

However, there was consternation when the old woman was unable to remember where she had hidden the money despite extensive searches by all parties to recover it.

As often happens in these situations, the finger of suspicion – particularly with new in-laws on board – was pointed in each other's direction. It was a clear shootout as both my ancestors believed that the other brother had managed to get on the good side of the old woman and form a pact whereby they would keep all the money while pretending that she couldn't remember.

At the time, they were co-habiting as couples in the same house with their widowed mother. The younger one, obviously feeling the greater sense of anger and betrayal, and his new bride, decided to relocate to the dairy, which was a one-roomed building under the same roof as the homestead.

Almost immediately they extended two rooms on to the original edifice with the help of his wife's brothers so that they could have a home of sufficient size that it would be inhabitable and comfortable for the Ireland of the time.

It meant that the other brother, with an extra room, held on to the old woman as a lodger in what had one time been her house.

Not only was there no communication between the two houses as the months and years went by, but according to my aunt's accounts, even neighbours had to select which door to knock on for visits. You could be a friend of one or other but not both.

It meant that the fission of the missing money had a longer and more widespread effect than could ever have been imagined.

Amusingly, it even percolated all the way down to the hens on 'the street' (the name given to the path immediately in front of the houses). Not known as one of the cleverest of God's creatures, the fowl nevertheless came to know which house to come running to when one or other of the women emerged outside with their meal. This understanding among the flock followed severe tutoring by whichever wife 'stood on guard' to ensure that it was only her layers which got the nourishment she was supplying.

There was no thawing within the two families over the years, despite the fact that often the brothers would milk their own cows in the common cowshed, and feed pigs in the pigshed without as much as a grunt to each other.

So there was no quarter given over the years and even when the old woman passed away, one side of the family honoured her death – (the brother with whom she lived) – while the other and his family went to the church and grave part of the ceremony but aside from that went about their work as though the lady was not related.

As it transpired, around the time of her first anniversary, another disappearance brought the family back into something remotely related to verbal contact.

The wife of the brother who had decamped to the dairy end of the building was surprised one evening when calling her chickens to find that the most prolific layer in her brood was nowhere to be seen.

Like every walk of life, the animal kingdom produces its own champions – one cow will fill a bucket with milk while another's best effort might be less than half that volume. Similarly some hens are infrequent contributors to a farm's economy, laying maybe a few times per week or laying for a week on end and then stopping for as long a length of time before producing eggs again.

The hen in question was always first in the race at feeding time but also contributed virtually every day as she could be seen in the most visible nest which was located in the annexe of the turf-shed.

When the brother arrived in from the fields where he was working that evening, his wife immediately shared with him her missing hen worries. In such moments the first suspicion would normally fall on a fox but that was dismissed in this instance.

It was the lambing season and stealing a new-born out on the hilly fields was much easier for the fox than risking entry to a farmyard and escaping with a screeching chicken amid the ferocious cacophony kicked up in the hen-house when such an unwelcome visitor calls.

Both husband and wife looked intently at each other as for the first time it dawned on them that perhaps there was a new era of thieving from next door – on their livestock.

This was not an unnatural conclusion from a couple who already carried the genuinely-held belief that their next-door neighbours had already 'codded' them out of over a hundred pounds which the mother had supposedly hidden but which was never found.

Initially, the couple decided to check out every nook and cranny of the farmyard to see if the hen could be located; the all-embracing search proved unsuccessful.

The other couple, both from afar and also from behind the curtain of their kitchen window, watched their neighbours take hours out of their day combing the garden, the orchards, the sheds, the barn and the haggard area.

"What are they looking for?" they asked themselves. "What could they have lost."

"Perhaps a ring or something personal and valuable," suggested the wife.

"No," said her partner, "it is something bigger than that... what in God's name could it be?"

It led to intrigue aplenty in that house while the other household was trying to cope with a rising anger and what they were now convinced was a definite loss.

"If it is a hen this week, what will it be next?" they mused as they sat either side of the fire at night-time, drinking their tea and hot cake before turning in for a restless night worrying about their future while lying side by side in the bed.

Following the death of the old woman, there came a time when the wife in that house thought it proper to go through what clothes and other personal items remained – a ritual with the twofold goal of getting rid of the clutter in her room while hopefully uncovering a previously hidden treasure – the money.

This wife had not liked the old woman one bit, however she had no choice but to live with her. She found her condescending and worse, she was a person who put no stór on keeping either herself or her room clean.

One morning, the young wife decided that it was time to throw out much of what remained and to 'air' and redecorate the room for her twin children who were still infants.

Like many homes of that time, there was only a front door on their house. Due to the situation with the other family, this meant she had to carry several baskets of old, musty material around the gable-end of the house to the north of their dwelling and prepare it for a fire which she planned to light that afternoon.

She worked hard and was delighted to stumble on some nice brooches and family photographs at the bottom of a cupboard. She decided she would put them in the loft for safe-keeping. It was an unusual house in that the middle one of their three rooms had an open area where a makeshift ladder could be put up the wall, allowing the climber access to the full loft of the older part of building.

This area, she remembered, had been searched inch by inch at the time of the money's disappearance and as she looked around with the benefit of a tilly-lamp she thought that lump sum was probably never going to be discovered.

Her husband had come in for his dinner at one o'clock delighted at the progress his wife had made through the morning. Before heading back to work the fields with the horse in the afternoon, he went up to where she had amassed all the rubbish for the fire and told her to wait a while until the wind changed from a direction which would blow the smoke away from the dwellings.

In late-afternoon and with all the other house chores done, she decided to feed the fowl a little earlier than usual so that she could go up and guard over sparks in case they landed on the thatched roof of the houses.

The dry nature of the old clothing and the wood-wormed state of the cupboards she had broken up and put on the fire as kindling and firewood meant that the flames licked skywards quickly and with alarming strength beyond what she had envisaged.

Concerned at the nature of the fire, she ran to the well where she filled a bucket with water which she threw into the middle of the mini inferno in the hope of dampening it.

It failed.

She remembered two old mattresses which they had thrown out at the back of the house some months earlier and ran there, dragging them one by one back to where the fire was still gaining height.

Summoning all her might, she flipped the first half-sodden old mattress into the middle of the pyre and then ran to bring the other. They had the effect of dousing the flames although sending a pungent plume of black smoke in the direction of the two front doors.

Her twin boys were sleeping in the makeshift playpen in the kitchen and her immediate thought was for their safety. She rushed to close the two half doors on her own entrance.

Her head was awhirl with worry as she knew the other house would be overcome with similar fumes unless the wife there did what she herself had just done and sealed the doors and windows.

As her children slept and she waited with a foreboding pain in her heart, her curiosity was aroused by a scraping noise coming from an area roof-high from somewhere in the back of the thatch.

As she listened more intently, she thought she could

THE LIE OF THE LAND

make out the 'kwawk, kwawk, kwawk' sound of a hen in distress – obviously the smoke had discommoded more than the humans around the place.

Then it hit her like a ton of bricks.

So that was the reason the other pair had been scouring around – it was looking for a clocking hen which had disappeared. She reasoned this to herself as she continued to work out where the hen might be located from the sound coming to her.

'Clocking' was the name given to hens around our part of the world which wanted to brood and become mothers to chicks by hatching on a nest full of eggs. They would find an out-of-the-way place for safety so that they could spend the time without interruption on the eggs.

Caught somewhere between relief in understanding this mystery and the guilt at the current gassing of her neighbour, the wife in the original house felt she should approach the other woman as soon as the smoke abated.

She gently knocked on the door which was opened suspiciously by the other wife who had a makeshift handkerchief to her nose area.

The woman outside explained and apologised for the fire, then mentioned the noise she had just heard from somewhere between the houses and wondered was it the clocking hen that the other family had been looking for?

The thought that the hen was alive immediately brought light to the eyes of the woman and for the first time in six years, she spoke and also accompanied her back into the main house.

From there they decided to go out the back to explore

if there was some sort of hidden crevice which they didn't know about where the hen had hidden during this time of incubation.

When they arrived at the back, they found quite an amount of ivy overrunning that area of the building. The house had a number of stone-masoned beams acting as support to the old back wall which had been built in the early 1800s and on top of one of these, the ivy managed to hide an opening which the hen had found.

There were two of those supports close together in the middle of the long wall and as the two wives peeled back the ivy, the sounds coming from the hen grew louder.

"There she is," said the wife who was its owner, as she pulled several little branches out of the wall to reveal a very strange view of a hen's tail.

As they continued to take away the ivy, they found that there was a hidden space about two feet square created when a previous extension had been worked on. The hen was able to access it by walking up the two mattresses which had been stacked adjacent to it up to less than an hour previously. While the ivy had hidden the space to the eye, it did not prevent entry and in fact was the perfect screen for this animal as she went about hiding herself from the world as she hatched her eggs into chickens.

To ensure a better footing as they examined the hen's nest, the wife in the main house fetched the ladder from inside and told the other woman that as it was her hen, she should go up to see if the eggs had hatched yet.

With a little trepidation at what she might find, the

woman slowly climbed up rung by rung, talking to the hen in a manner that she would have done while keeping sentry during their feeding time.

She slowly put her right hand under the hen and began feeling around the nest. As she did so, she mentally checked back and realised it was over three weeks since her best layer had disappeared.

At exactly the same time as she had calculated that it was over the 21 days, she felt the first little ball of fur, then another, then another.

She gave a squeal of delight and told the other woman the good news. For the first time the two women were not just communicating but helping each other out. The woman on the ground had brought back one of the old woman's baskets and put in a bed of straw to receive the chickens one by one as they were handed down to her.

Six newly-born chicks were handed down the ladder from one brother's wife to the other and left in a circle in the basket which would serve as their new nest.

The two women knew that lifting the clocking hen down would be a little more difficult because of her size and the fact that the woman on the ladder only had one free hand with which to catch her as she used the other to hold her balance at all times.

The hen became slightly disoriented as, hearing her chicks chirping from below and with the woman's hand trying to grab her behind her wing area, she let out a loud series of 'kwawks' and attempted to raise herself up on her legs in the confined area.

Scratching her claws into the nest, she began to furiously thrash around as panic descended upon her.

Feathers, bits of broken egg shell and some old thatching began to fly through the air and down on the ground.

The wife on the ground put her body in front of the basket to protect the chicks when suddenly the hen's leg caught something from further back in the nest and sent flying like an exocet towards the ground. It hit the woman standing underneath on the head before ricocheting into the basket, instantly crushing the chickens as they huddled together. The hen flew out of the hold flapping furiously as she turned to see where her chicks were located.

The women watched as the hen approached the chicks. She circled them several times before sitting on them, each propped up by the limp body beside it. Confused, she rounded her wing over them within a matter of seconds as she would have done if they were alive.

Having watched this without speaking, both women's attention then settled on the old box which after squashing the newly hatched chicks, had come to rest against the side of the basket.

Instantly and instinctively they knew what it was and what it contained.

This time the secret within the box had exacted a price, but it was nothing like the penalty the family had paid since the first time it went missing.

6

The Land Grabbers

MY understanding of our family tree on the paternal side is that we arrived from Tipperary just after the famine and had been living on our farm for just over 100 years when I was born.

Often as a child I can remember talk about who were the oldest families in the town and in the townlands around us. We were considered one of the older ones according to the elders and one of our uncles, by marriage that is, had the claim of being descended from the oldest family in the entire area.

While times and attitudes have changed to varying degrees depending on the areas in the present day, back then stuff like that mattered. As any rural person will tell you the term 'blow in' is one of the most belittling and cutting that can be hurled at people in a community.

New farmers in the area were almost on trial for the first quarter of a century; even then they were still 'blow ins' if there were hard words spoken in some instances, but it would be accepted that they were half-way there in putting down roots if they survived for another 25 years or so.

I'm not sure of the history behind 'The Sally Gardens', the fields my grandfather bought from his immediate neighbour after his first 50 years settling into the area. According to what I heard from older neighbours, there was a friendship between my grandfather and the man who sold him the land.

When that neighbour passed on, he left the rest of his farm to his three daughters, all of whom remained spinsters for the course of their lives. While the land was less than two miles from our local town, back then that was well out in the country; in fact it was verging on the remote.

The family of the three women kept their own company with only the very occasional call to houses in and around them.

Apparently when they were growing up – slightly younger than my father – they were quite friendly to him and his brothers, but as the years went by, they became obsessed with a belief that we had grabbed (stolen) their land.

What I am about to write may sound unbelievable but because I experienced it myself, I can assure you it is true.

During certain new moons in the calendar, our gates

would be opened and cattle moved out of the fields during the night so that my father often had to spend a large part of the following day trying to round up the cattle who may have gone in with neighbours' animals or just kept walking the bog road for two or three miles.

When there was no television and little radio in a house, there was seldom a shortage of talking by the adults about the various subjects which cropped up on a periodic basis. When the disappearance of our cattle occurred, it became the centre of our conversation.

Incredibly my father never got upset – his only concern was that the straying cattle might cause an accident with cars.

We often would bump into these women on the road in the course of a working day. My father always said 'hello'. They never answered but would look threateningly in our direction. He didn't seem to take any notice, but I did.

To be truthful they terrified me; I always felt they were warning me with those looks that some day they would make me pay for what they believed was the injustice my father's father had carried out on them.

Two of the sisters stayed around the house and yard and seldom ventured out except to make hay in the field beside the Sally Gardens.

The middle sister was big and reminded me of an Indian chief the way she rode her bike. With her dark skin and piercing eyes, I expected her to say 'how' as much as 'why' if she ever deigned to talk to me.

These women brought daily terror into my young life. At seven years of age I was given a second hand blue bike for my birthday; part of the deal was that I would cycle the mile-and-a-half from our house to bring the cows home from where most of our land was located. We had one field near the yard but it wasn't big enough for them to graze in both day and night, unless we were content to have very little milk in our churn.

My worst fears were realised one lovely July evening when I arrived at the Sally Gardens' gate to bring the cows home at around six o'clock.

There in the adjoining field I could plainly see the three sisters turning hay. Talk about panic. I had our dog with me but knew that if he barked when rounding up the cows, they would be alerted that I was there – and all by myself at that.

I suppose needs must when the wolf is at the door. I tied the dog to my bike with twine which my father had used to hold up a diagonal piece of wood onto the gate. I ordered the dog to 'sit'. Fortunately, the one thing the Sally Gardens had was cover – rushes all across its 12 Irish acres and furze in the upper field.

I opened the wooden gates in total silence and immediately, like a paratrooper, fell on my knees to take up the cover of the rush clumps.

I started to do something which I suppose in hindsight was akin to ventriloquism – I was throwing my voice to reach the cows by calling – 'home, girls, home' in the hope that they would pick up my signal while the three sisters the other side of the ditch wouldn't hear.

The cows were normally slow about making their way to the gate because they preferred to eat the grass instead of walking the long distance home.

That particular day I was sure that they sensed my problem and were even less co-operative than usual.

By then the dog had chewed through the twine and charged out into the middle of the field barking out orders to the cows to shift or they would get a bite on their back legs.

Fortunately by that stage, despite 'walking' on my hands and knees, there were several bushes to mask my presence. I saw the sisters put down their forks and come over to the side of the drain between our lands to see what was happening. The dog knew his job and was carrying it out expertly. As he drove the cows towards the gate, I resumed a mad scramble on all fours in that direction too and once the 12 cows had gone through out onto the road, I leapt up, closed the gate, jumped on my bike and began shouting like a madman to gee-up the cows' pace.

I didn't look back until we passed the nearest house where the woman I called Aunt Maggie lived. I knew I was safe once I got that far because if they were following me – and they weren't – I would have got her to protect me.

One other day some time later I was convinced the middle sister was going to kill me at the head of the road. My father had sent me to open a gate. When I returned to the river bridge, there was no sign of him. She got down off her bike and appeared to be about to head in my direction when I screamed at the top of my voice: "Daddy, Daddy, she's coming to get me."

Miraculously and immediately, my father appeared from under the bridge where he had been filling a bucket with water and I ran behind him for safety.

He just nodded to the woman to recognise her presence when I thought he should have at least threatened to kill her if she ever looked at me again. As I said, I could never understand his patience and forbearance when it came to those three sisters.

Even when I had another decade of years on my back and had grown to be over six feet tall by then, there was a residual feeling of discomfort in my system any time I met them on the road. I was totally confident by then that physically I would be able to fight back or run away from them so the gut-wrenching pain of meeting them was not nearly as acute as it was when I was smaller.

But it was still there.

My father got sick the summer of my 18th year, meaning my brother and I had to do most of the haysaving and tillage minding down on the farm.

That was a year where we got a rare hot summer which meant we had the hay in early, or at least early for us – something which was a great relief to my father.

One day when we were working at getting the barley field ready for the combine to come in by picking up stones or bits of branches which might damage its inner mechanisms, our attention was drawn to the sound of a fire brigade siren in the distance. When it turned from the main road up our way, we wondered where the fire might be as there was no sign of smoke on the horizon.

To our surprise, the tender pulled in at the house of the three sisters and then proceeded to drive down into one of their back fields.

We went back to our work, which also involved lifting up any bits of lodged barley by using a four-grained fork to twist it upright, or as upright as we could manage it.

As we worked with our backs to the sisters' farm, we got into a rhythm which saw us cover ground very quickly. About half an hour after the fire brigade arrived, one of their crew came into our field and approached us.

"There's a big cow, I'd say she's nearly a ton, in a boghole over there," he explained. "The women say she's been there for a few days and will die if we don't get her out now. But it's sunk so low that we can't get any of our ropes around it to get a grip."

The man who was talking was a hero of mine – he was a great footballer and I had started to play for the local senior team with him.

"We'd love to help," my brother said (not taking my feelings into account with that remark), "but the truth is they don't talk to us and if we as much as put a foot on their land, they'd do a dance until we got off it."

The footballer looked at my brother and then me. "Look, the three of them are crying over there and this is the only cow they have to keep milk on the table for them. Would you not help?"

Reluctantly we went over, not that we didn't want to help but because we felt sure we would be given short shrift when they saw us.

As it turned out, the opposite was the case. The sisters smiled when the fire brigade man who was the footballer told them that we had come over to offer assistance.

You didn't have to travel far in our district to find farms where moorland was actually reclaimed bog and

THE LIE OF THE LAND

dangerous in certain parts for cattle to graze on. In this instance, the cow had followed a fresh lick of grass into the marshy area and had got bogged down in a blind boghole.

The fire brigade lads were 'townies' and had no real clue as to how to go about taking the animal out of the predicament she was in. Seeing the situation, my brother took charge, telling me to jump in at the tail while he began manoeuvring a short tree branch under the cow's head to force her to look up.

He went above and beyond the call of duty, stripping down to his pants to get the rope, which he had doubled up, down underneath her front legs at the start of her belly. That meant submerging himself in the boghole beside her – a dangerous thing to do if she somehow came over on top of him.

He then crossed over to her other side and again by submerging virtually all of himself for a few moments, he was able to catch the other end of the rope and pull it up into his hands. Once he had done that, he made a loop knot on the cow's shoulders, threw the rope to the firemen and told them to pull.

I had done very little at the rear but in time-honoured fashion, lifted her tail and shouted like mad in the hope that it would encourage the beast to make an effort to extricate herself from the glue she was submerged in.

Earlier the firemen dug as directed by my brother to lower the edge of the hole, making it easier for the cow to lunge forward. When they began to pull, a massive slurping sound rumbled from underneath the cow indicating to us that she was using her legs.

That was important because it meant she was still interested in getting out and had not been totally deflated by her vain efforts from the previous two days. After a series of pulls by the men, the big Hereford's body finally began to rise up and as she caught hold of the firmer land, her own legs were still strong enough to help her exit the danger.

She was a quiet beast and didn't flinch as we unroped her and led her down by the ditch to a higher field at the back of their house. On our way back, the sisters thanked us profusely. "God bless you both, God bless you," they repeated in unison.

I was extremely happy about all of that – though when I told my father in his sick bed that night about the ending of the enmity between them and us, he replied with the hint of a smile: "I wouldn't be so sure about that."

Within 24 hours, I knew what he meant. I was at the Sally Gardens' gate coming out from the field as the middle sister approached on her bike. "Good evening," I said warmly but was dismayed that she turned her head in a highly exaggerated manner to the other side and pedalled her bike away at speed.

The message was clear – yesterday was yesterday, today is a new day as far as they were concerned.

Shortly afterwards my father passed away – suddenly in my eyes – though local people said they noticed that he had been failing for some time. I was only a child when my mother died and I remember the pain I felt at her loss. I had the comfort then of knowing my father was still there – that was now gone.

On the morning of his funeral Mass, I thought my

heart would explode in my chest. Obviously I was by then more mature and understood the reality of losing a man who had given up so much so that my brother and I could have a future away from the subsistence of our farm. He allowed us go away to boarding school for five years and lived alone through that time except when we were home on holidays.

I kept my head low right through the ceremony and even when the poor priest forgot my father's first name when praying especially for him after Holy Communion, I kept my eyes focused on the ground in front of me rather than looking up at him on the altar to demonstrate the anger that I felt there and then.

In our diocese, after a funeral Mass there was a tradition that people who knew the deceased or their family would go up to the coffin, leave a Mass card and money in a basket as a sign of their friendship.

They would then walk along the front pew shaking the hands of the next of kin. It meant that there was often a queue up the middle aisle of the church which could last up to an hour before it cleared.

I was beside my brother and my uncles and aunts in the front pew. Out of curiosity, I turned around about 20 minutes into this particular procession to see if it would go on for much longer. To my surprise, I saw the middle sister, the one who did the shopping and attended funerals on the others' behalf, some way down the church with a white envelope in her hand.

She stared straight at me without showing any recognition and every time I checked thereafter, I saw her waiting patiently in the queue as it inched forward.

When she came close to the top of the church near the coffin, I watched intently as she put her right hand on the lid for a brief moment, then she dropped the Mass Card onto it and put 50p into the basket alongside.

After that she turned around and unlike anyone else there walked back down the church while the other mourners turned left to shake our hands as they shuffled across the front of the church.

It was commented on afterwards with implied criticism that she had seriously slighted my father and us.

The more I've thought about it since, the more I am inclined to take the opposite view; she had honoured his death with her attendance and had in her own way said her goodbye by touching the coffin.

Whatever hatchet there was between him and the sisters was buried in that moment.

However, as for the rest of us – the living part of his family – now that was a different matter entirely. We were still fair game for their indignation – and as it transpired we got plenty of it too.

7

To Catch A Rat

THE rat terrorised us all winter long in the barn which was adjacent to the backdoor of our house. I used to have nightmares about it sneaking into my room in the dead of night and getting into the bed beside me.

My mother went off her food and never once stepped out into 'the street' in front of our doorway.

My father used to give out to us all about living on a farm and yet being afraid of a little rodent. But behind his putdown we all knew that he too hated rats.

My mother said it was in his blood. His father had died from a fall off his beloved horse when it shied away and leapt into a ditch with the fright it got from a rat crossing the road in front of him. My grandfather, who loved

THE LIE OF THE LAND

horses, fell awkwardly from the grey stallion he used as a means of transport and hit his head on a rock in the ditch. He was brought home unconscious by a neighbour who was riding with him.

He never recovered and a month later my father at 14 years of age was brought into life in a man's world with his own father hardly cold in the grave.

His mother and people around our farm seemingly spoke a lot about the accident as if it was part of a daily memorial pageant. For years it was the talk of the locality as people recalled how unfortunate we were to have lost a man in his prime because of a rat.

My mother thought it was even worse luck when an animal that had already killed one of our kith and kin should be back in the centre of our lives tormenting us.

She was a devout Catholic like virtually all the people who lived in small holdings around us, but there was a part of her which believed in superstition and maybe even reincarnation.

Every time my father met a neighbour at this time, the conversation would invariably stray towards the rat and my father's admission that he could not catch it, no matter what he tried.

And boy did he try. The trap was the first source of annoyance as Mr Rat was able to spring it somehow and then take the rasher of bacon or whatever other enticement had been put there.

Then my father tried to flush him out from the back of the barn with the terrier dog barking and smelling ferociously. But he refused to budge.

The cat was a particular disappointment as it failed

to show any interest in acknowledging that the vermin was even hiding somewhere within the four walls. Even worse, she had taken to climbing the tree out the back of the barn, trying to nab the blackbirds and robins which had nests in the surrounding smaller trees and the swallows who had theirs built on the rafters of the cow shed, which was in the flight path of the big tree as well.

My mother's sister up the road had given us the cat as a kitten, saying it had come from the best 'ratter' she had ever bred.

The geography of our farmyard was very much in favour of an air traffic control lazy cat or a rat who knew the ins and outs to the barn via the old gable end wall. That same wall was a problem. Built by our forebears maybe a century before, it had cracked and was full of nooks and crannies. My father estimated that it was three feet thick and built at a time when every sort of solid item was used to make a building steady.

He got the loan of a blow torch from the garage man in the village in a bid to burn the rat out of his cosy hiding place. But it either dodged the flames or had a particular hiding place to guard against such an incendiary device.

After each failed venture, my father often went quiet for hours on end and it might be after our supper when we were sitting around the fire that he would engage us with his thoughts on the unseen foe.

"Only I hear him make his escape every time I open the door of the barn, I'd say I'm mad and there is no rat there at all," he'd say.

He had tried leaving the door of the barn open and sneaking in to catch the thief of his winter feed red-handed but the sound of a footstep was all the warning Mr Rat needed to beat a hasty retreat before harm could come to him.

My uncle who was a much bigger and more modern farmer came to visit my mother, his sister-in-law and jeered when my father told him the tale of his misfortune.

"Good God man, have you never heard of poison? I do it all the time and I never have a problem with them dirty yokes."

Before my mother could even offer him a cup of tea, he jumped onto his tractor, drove over to his farm where my mother had been raised and was back in our kitchen within half an hour.

He took out a container from his coat pocket and asked my mother for some polish tins which she kept for a variety of reasons once they were empty.

She gave him two large half tins and two smaller ones. I followed my uncle with excitement mounting inside me as he placed the tins where he estimated the rat entered and had created 'runs' to shelter him from visibility.

He told my father to make sure the barn doors were closed at all times or it could kill the terrier or the cat, who my mother said wasn't worth the gunpowder that would shoot her because she hadn't even shown any inclination to do her job.

The next morning my father came in to inform my mother that there had been no noise when he opened the door on the barn. "Maybe that stuff has worked," he said with a smile breaking across his face.

"Thanks be to God," said my mother. "Sure I always

knew my side of the family was where the brains were, even if only through marriage."

The two smiled at one another and as my father went off to feed the calves, cows and pigs, my mother began doing her household chores with a lighter heart than she had felt for ages.

"I'm delighted about that," she said aloud to herself, as my brother and I watched her from the table where we were finishing our breakfast. "I think that rat would have driven that man demented if it went on much longer," she added, addressing no one in particular.

She then walked over to the two of us and kissed us on the tops of our heads, repeating what she had said as if we hadn't been present to hear her the first time.

That evening my uncle was over again and when my mother told him there had been no sign of the rat since he laid the poison, he was delighted.

"Oh yes, that poison gives them a terrible death. They eat it up and then they get this awful thirst and drink themselves to death trying to quench the fire in the belly. I'd say you'll have a shortage of water by the time your man in the barn is finished."

He went out to the barn, saw where one or two of the tins had been disturbed, as he put it, and the one nearest the rat's entry point had been knocked over and spilled.

"You know I'd say he ate feck all of it but you only need a small amount. It's lethal stuff, this is," he explained, pointing to the material he had brought back in on one of the big polish tins from the barn."

My mother told him to bring the rest home with him as it would be her luck to poison the dog. She wouldn't mind poisoning the cat, she added, but it would be on her conscience for killing one of God's creatures.

"Sure isn't the rat one of them too," joked my uncle.

"Oh them dirty things were put on earth by the devil to torment us," she said as she wrinkled up her nose and gave a visible shiver at the thought of her greatest torment in life.

My father reported back to us in the kitchen every morning as if he was preparing a bulletin for the news on the wireless. "No sign again this morning," he would say, before closing the door and going off about his business.

It was the same for four days – he would go out with his buckets, open the barn door, listen for a minute and then return to the back door, open it, give the good news and go on into his day.

It was with immense surprise, as you can imagine when on the fifth day, he landed back in the middle of the kitchen's concrete floor with a look of pain on his face.

"He's back," he said, as if it was Jesse James he had confronted outside.

My mother let the sod of turf she held in her hand fall limply on the ground and even I stopped eating to listen to what he was saying.

"I don't believe you," my mother said, making the sign of the cross while speaking.

My father pushed his flat cap back on his head and scratched his head several times as if he was massaging his annoyance away.

"No sooner did I open the door than I heard the rustling sound that I thought was gone forever. Poison or no poison but this boy is alive and kicking and back to drive us all mad," he complained.

He got to the door and seeing my mother's eyes following him, said sarcastically. "Your side of the family have great brains all right."

My uncle returned the next evening and put down the poison and we watched the tins to see how much of the stuff the rat picked.

He now knew not to eat it, my uncle said, so he would set a trap.

"You have to out-think these fellas or they'll ate you out of house and home," he emphasised as he pulled on the butt of his cigarette.

Early the next morning, I went out to the back of the haggard where I could see both the front entrance to the barn and the back, favoured by you know who. I saw my father open the barn door and within a second I saw the rustle of grass at the back of the barn which I knew was the rat making his escape.

Before I had time to work out in my own head how I might catch the fleeing rodent, the sight of our cat, the same lazy, good-for-nothing that both my parents hated, flying off the top branch of the beech tree, caught my attention.

I could see its ears pricked as it sailed through the air with its eyes locked on the prey below. I knew before I saw anything further that it had hit its quarry spot-on as it landed because the squeal from the rat split the morning air.

By the time I had gotten up off my haunches and ran down to the back of the barn from the hayshed, the rat was already dead. Its head hung loosely from where the cat had broken its neck with its jump.

As I arrived at the same time as my father from the barn and my mother from the kitchen, the cat was busy using its paw to rake over the rat's body. It then flicked him in the air with remarkable agility and caught it in its mouth and began walking out past the front of the barn and in to the street at the front of the house.

My parents and myself were silent witnesses to the early-morning drama. The cat appeared to take on a haughty swagger as it walked into centre stage with the rat, shaking the dead carcass from side to side in our view before depositing it onto the ground right in front of the door.

My father put his arm around my mother's shoulders and gave her a big hug. The cat walked up, tail erect between the two of them and rubbed off my father's wellington boots and then my mother's nylon stockings, purring loudly as she did so.

It was almost as if she was rebuking them for doubting that she had climbed the tree to kill birds instead of planning how to catch the creature that had caused us so much trouble.

8

The Tractor *versus* The Horse

MY father was in his fifties when I was born – he was the eldest of seven children and his own father died when he was 14.

He helped his mother raise the other six children as if he was a parent which probably was at least partially responsible for putting off marriage until well into his fifth decade on earth.

In most ways I never noticed that he was older than our relations' fathers. He loved reading, western films and heavyweight boxing and would talk all day about any of those subjects just like the other fathers around where we grew up.

He had a graphic way of explaining things – for instance the night Max Schmeling knocked out the great Joe Louis in the first round, my father's memory was that he had only one leg in his trousers running down the stairs when those in the kitchen surrounding the radio listening to the BBC broadcast on a crackly dial called out to him to go back to bed because the fight was over.

He studied the 'Tale of the Tape' in the Evening Herald before every big fight and could be guaranteed nearly always to give the right verdict. He went against the grain to say that Floyd Patterson would beat Ingemar Johansson in the rematch and later was sure that Sonny Liston would knock the living daylights out of Patterson when they met for the heavyweight championship of the world in the Madison Square Gardens. He was right on both counts.

Cassius Clay, later to become Muhammad Ali, threw him. My father was convinced he wouldn't last a round against Liston and was gobsmacked to find out the next day that Clay had won.

For a man who loved current affairs in both politics and sport, he was very much a traditionalist when it came to farming. While my uncle had a grey Ferguson tractor, my father had a mare (Molly), a horse (Benny) and a pony (Dolly) for all his work and transport on the farm.

He would point to the cost of diesel, of needing services, new tyres and batteries and say that a man would end up working most days of the week solely to keep those machines ticking over.

"All I need is to give the horses and pony grass, water

and a little oats and hay and they will do all the work I need."

My uncle used to 'rise' him about being an 'Amish-type' farmer – a term I didn't understand as a child but felt it had a derogatory connotation – which of course it had. It meant he was backward thinking and my cousins, who obviously sided with their father, would say we were old fashioned farmers.

That was one of the first times I felt a little ashamed of my dad – why couldn't he be just like other fathers and have tractors and trailers, buckrakes and mowing-arms instead of horses and carts, ponies and traps and gig-rakes to row up the hay.

The two families worked the land side by side with the tools of two different generations.

I don't for one minute want anyone to think though that there was any real enmity between the two men or us – in fact, in some ways having the two methods were a plus for both sides.

For instance as the two farms comprised of hilly fields, it was much more practical for the mare and plough to work there, while on the flat, the two socks of the plough was quicker to cover ground than the single plough which the mare pulled.

Molly was supremely strong and while Benny was the elder statesman, he was really only yoked-up to do light work such as pull out loads of dung from the yard to the fields.

Dolly the pony was the roadhog... she was our car and the clip-clop of her feet made journeys short for the years I grew up with her on the farm.

The year I made my First Holy Communion was particularly wet in the winter and spring months, meaning the moor soil on most of our low-lying land was very wet.

Even the month of May, when those working the land normally expected a respite from the inclemency of the weather, was spiteful in its cold and wet offerings. Growth was retarded and tillage was well behind – though with the mixture of horse and tractor, the two farms had managed better than most.

This was the month where the turf work began in the bog. Two houses with fires down every day of the year needed a lot of sods – to cook, and heat the homes.

Normally we began cutting the two banks of turf on the same day and 'quit' at the same time each evening to go off and do the yard chores such as feeding and milking at the different homesteads.

The two mothers came down for this ritual and we as kids were allowed take a day or two off school to help with the catching and the spreading of the sods across pre-ordained areas which were dry, or as dry as was possible, under foot.

After a week on the bog, it was the Saturday where the elders took stock of how much turf was cut, how much of it would be quality or 'puckie' (light brown stuff which would burn very quickly) and more importantly if there was sufficient amounts to see us through the following 12 months.

The seven children had been particularly helpful that year in pushing the bogey (bog cart) out to help Molly and at times to lend our weight to the mud-guards to push the grey Ferguson through the quagmire which had been created by the traffic as it journeyed out from the turf bank with loads for us to spread.

We always 'drummed up' (lit a fire and made tea and sandwiches) around two o'clock on the bog. That Saturday evening was quite miserable with a greyish-blue drizzle coming across from the west making the grass and vegetation on the bog very slippery. We went across to an overhanging tree to find shelter during the meal.

The mood was glum and there was still a sight of work to complete before we could cut for home where another hour's work was ahead of us in milking the cows and feeding the calves and the pigs.

Despite having only one horse power – Molly – we had managed to get our loads out more efficiently through the day and by five o'clock, my father had finished with his slean and our crew were cheerfully spreading out the last load onto the drier ground a few hundred yards away.

As we got ready to pack up our coats and left-over food, we said our goodbyes to our cousins who looked downhearted that they still had another trailer load to bring out and spread before they were finished.

My father, who had directed my older brother to put the pony under the trap, was unyoking the mare at the side as the tractor pulled out that final load towards the rushes at the higher end of the bog.

Not for the first time the engine had to work hard to keep the wheels turning going through a gap which had become increasingly quicksand-like from all the churning. My uncle, who was driving, felt his engine losing momentum and pulled down on the hand-throttle to give it more power. The two back wheels fought for every ounce of earth to find grip but the more they dug in, the greater the swill of black, watery liquid they threw up in the air.

We all ran to push but by the time we got there the wheels had sunk quite low into the ground and were spinning freely without giving any forward trajectory.

The wonderfully rhythmic litany of curses my uncle unleashed as he banged his hand down angrily on the steering wheel told its own story – the tractor was no longer an engine, it was a helpless inanimate object, just like the trailer it had been endeavouring to pull.

Amid all the mayhem and the turmoil, my father slipped almost unnoticed past us and was busily tying a rope to the front of the tractor. He put back on the mare's collar, hames and put two large knots on either sides of the rope so that they held in the hames' clasps. Before that he measured out the length of each side after he had lapped the rope under the front of the tractor frame.

We all fell silent as we watched him concentrate on his work. When he was finished, he walked the mare up to where the ropes were about to become taut and steadied her by holding her winkers from the front. As he did so, he told my uncle to start up the tractor and to put it in gear when he saw the mare make her effort to pull.

My uncle leapt into the seat and within seconds had the tractor purring. He signalled to my father to let him know that he was ready for action.

My father gave a little smile to accompany his thumbs-up to him.

"Go, girl, go," he urged Molly gently, as he gave a reassuring pat to the white blaze on the horse's nose.

The mare's broad black chest expanded as she prepared for the exertion; instinctively she lowered her head as she simultaneously used the power of her hind quarters to begin the rescue job.

The two mothers, the seven children, the workman and the four dogs all looked at what was happening as if they were stilled, like a picture in a frame.

The tractor roared as my uncle sought to give whatever assistance he could; the mare gave an almighty grunt through her two nostrils and the tractor and trailer began to shake and slowly move forward.

The mare tilted her body again and a second almighty grunt was the sign that she was about to dig in for her supreme effort. The tractor wheels were still spinning but with the mare's power on their side, they had no choice but to go forward. As she strained her limbs with her pull, the tractor began to find its own grip and once the wheels were clear of the gap and up on drier ground, they powered the vehicle forward under its own power once again.

It was then my father said: "Woh, girl, woh."

Molly obeyed.

All the human bystanders cheered as if she had won the Aga Khan Cup; the dogs barked and Molly surveyed us with her ears pricked and an intelligence in her eye which made you feel she understood what was going on.

My uncle, who was my father's biggest tease down the years about how he farmed, opened his packet of Woodbine, lit up with a great sense of relief in his smile as he took a long drag on his cigarette.

"Sometimes, the old ways are best," he conceded as he shook my father's hand in gratitude. "Without Molly, we'd have been here til dark trying to offload the turf and get the tractor out."

"Aye, God Bless her, but she's as strong a horse as I've ever seen working," my father said with more than a little pride in his mare.

My mother and all of us were animated as we recalled the exploits we had just witnessed Molly perform as we started for home. My father had waited until we were up on the bog road before lighting up his pipe and was now smoking contentedly.

He said nothing all the way home but every now and again my mother would look over at him and he would smile at her – a smile beyond words or embellishment.

The moment found its own completeness in the silence.

9

The Scarecrow

HE did what he was supposed to do – he scared the crows.

This homemade man, stood somewhere around centre field in the wheat or the oats or the barley and kept the crows away from the crops – and earned his corn each summer and autumn in this fashion.

All that was needed to construct this valuable member of the farm was a few bits of wood set up like a cross, with a long topcoat hanging from it and of course a hat on top of a straw head.

That, together with a series of plastic streamers running up and down the field, was supposed to stop the crows from descending on the crop at times when there was no real human around to scare them off from desecrating the ears of grain.

Other people had more modern devices to keep the birds out of their fields... such as the annoying automatic shot sound of a gun which drove families mad until the threshing was done and they didn't have to worry about it for another year.

When I was very young my father had a shotgun which he used occasionally on the farm – if he saw a fox threatening the ewes or if he wanted to kill a rabbit to add to the menu from time to time.

He handed the gun over to the Guards when he came home one evening and found me using it as a prop with the rest of my cowboy uniform. It happened around that time that two people were accidentally shot in the area – one fatally and one who had a narrow escape.

It made sense for my father to remove such potential trouble from the house, particularly as my mother was on his case night and day until he caved in.

It coincided with a visit from my Dublin cousins to the house and my uncle, who was my father's younger brother, was larger than life itself. He decided to stay with us and brought his two boys down for a week, leaving his eldest son, his daughter and his Dublin-born wife, who hated the country except for a flying visit anyway, back at base.

For someone about seven or eight, it was like having the movies brought to your house when he was present. He never stopped telling us stories, all of which were fascinating because he was centrally involved. He was pals with 'Lugs' Brannigan, the renowned cop who had an old-fashioned way of dealing with the thugs he met on his beat.

'Lugs' was a one-man police force who kept law and order on the mean streets of Dublin.

He used my uncle as back-up on a number of his justice expeditions – most memorably when he turned three teenagers who were terrorising a local shopkeeper down a lane in the darkness where my uncle was waiting for them.

"Oh Lugs had the right idea, ok," said my uncle. "Those three gutties went back to their friends and said 'whatever you do stay away from that shop as we were knocked out down the lane from there last night.'"

My father had a love-hate relationship with him; he liked his effervescence and energy but it would annoy him that when recalling things that happened when they were young, his brother would wildly exaggerate what had actually happened.

Whatever about my father, neither my brother nor I had any reservations about my uncle – he was entertainment from one end of the day to the next.

His sons were not close to us in the same way that our cousins who we saw every day were but they were nice and besides, the Dublin accents were a curiosity in themselves.

And they undertook everything enthusiastically, whether it was rising water in our lower field for the cattle or sitting on the cocks of hay which the mare pulled in through the fields with chains as my father guided her with the reins.

My uncle was mechanically gifted and had things around our yard working which had been broken for ages... the light in the barn, the stopcock in the water supply which sporadically came from the mains but often failed to work.

He suggested that we should source our own water supply and said he knew where there was a spring underneath one part of our yard. He went out to the ditch, cut several hazel branches and made two of them like a Y. He told us to hold the two shorter stems in our hands and to go around the yard divining for water.

My brother found the spot and it was a major disappointment to me that even when I was shown where the water was underneath the earth, the stick refused to move towards my body from my outstretched arms as had happened with him.

He was fair in colouring and that was why he had the power to divine, my uncle explained.

That week was a whirlwind of action and interaction; we talked to neighbours I only barely knew because they were brothers or sisters of my uncle's friends when he was growing up; he walked miles down by the river and created makeshift fishing rods from long sticks, and catgut he had bought in the hardware shop. We caught seven perch and a trout which he snatched with a hook, having spotted the fish sleeping in the shadow under the side of the riverbank.

The night before my uncle and his sons were due to go back, my father raised in conversation the problems with the harvest. "Those crows are getting cleverer every year," he said in the kitchen as my mother served the nightly tea. "They don't seem to be afraid of the scarecrow any more."

He went on to relate amusingly how an old neighbour

felt the same years before when the birds had raided his potato drills. "I'll cod the buggers next year," he confided to my father. "I'm going to pretend to put in seedlings but I will put stones down instead. And that will fix their clock," he said. In fact, he felt so convinced that he did it.

Who was codding whom in that instance was indeed a moot point.

The chat about the crows was all my uncle needed to tell my brother and I to be ready to go down to the fields before light the next morning.

"We'll wait in the field for them and frighten the living daylights out of them if they attack the barley."

Although our shotgun had long since been decommissioned to the local garda station, my uncle said he knew an IRA man from his youth across the fields who would be only too happy to give him a loan of two guns and some ammunition. Even at the late hour that was in it, he jumped into his car and was gone to get the required arsenal for the following morning's activities. By the time he returned I had gone to bed and fallen asleep.

My mother had misgivings about us all going out at that hour of the morning with live ammunition and hoped the IRA man would have nothing to give us. If it was my father suggesting such activity, she would have put her foot down and that would have been the end of it. But she had such a soft spot for my uncle that she didn't make her objections public beyond pulling a disdainful face behind his back and praying for the non-delivery of the ammo that night.

We gathered in a small amphitheatre at the end of the field just as dawn was about to break. My uncle had us up out of bed and fed and transported on foot to the spot where he wanted us congregated for the big shoot.

Talk about excitement. This was Batman meeting The Virginian as far as I was concerned. Real guns, real shooting. Somehow pretend-cowboys and indians would never be the same again.

The caw-cawing in the distance whetted our appetites; the birds now were assembling for their early morning feed. We knew that they had lost all fear of Mr Scarecrow in the middle of the field, for whatever reason. Maybe they were a more intelligent murder of crows than our area had seen previously or maybe they had watched the inanimate man over a number of years and came to the conclusion that he was no threat to them.

With only two guns, there was a scramble in hushed voices among us to see who would fire the gun my uncle wasn't using. My brother was chosen, then my uncle decided his oldest boy present would get next crack at it, then the next and then... me.

That took away from the excitement as I figured by the time the four in front of me had fired two shots each, any self-respecting bird would have relocated to the next parish.

And so it came to pass. As the black cape of birds came across the horizon and hovered over our field, my uncle and my brother both got their shots off, dropping three of the birds.

My uncle then quickly reloaded both his and my brother's shotguns and handed them over to the next two in line. By then the birds were retreating whence they had come at breakneck speed. The two boys, three and five years older than me, shot their cartridges into the air but failed to bring down anything.

My uncle then took the nearest gun to him and loaded two more cartridges quickly and thrust the weapon into my hand. There was nothing left to fire at so I just handed it back to him with what I imagine was a sulky face on me.

"Quick, aim over there," he said, pointing at the scarecrow. I looked and saw one of the crows shot down in the first hail of bullets had landed on the shoulder of the scarecrow and was caught up in the plastic streamers which swayed in the early morning breeze like waves lapping across the cornfield.

"Shoot. Shoot it before it escapes," he ordered me animatedly.

I looked through the sight on the top of the gun and saw that the bird's fall had been broken by the plastic streamers tied around the scarecrow. I could see that one of the bird's legs had been snared and the bird was now trying with all its worth to free itself.

It flapped and flapped its wings violently before finally finding a balance on the shoulder of the old coat of the scarecrow.

My fingers twitched in anticipation of pulling the trigger when two things happened simultaneously which affected my concentration. As if it knew I could see it, the crow's eye went blank like he had hid it at the back of his socket in anticipation of my shot. The thought struck me too that if I managed to hit the bird, it would be the first time I'd killed anything in my life.

Those two things unnerved me as I pulled the trigger twice in quick succession. The scarecrow's makeshift head of straw and sticks and my father's old hat exploded like a halo on the impact of the first shot. Then the scarecrow's body swayed backwards before dropping after it had been hit with the second of my bullets.

There followed a loud fluttering of wings as the previously captured crow was released in the downing of the scarecrow.

We all looking on with our mouths open to see what had happened.

I felt mortified as slowly and deliberately the bird rose into the distance, its wings rising and falling rhythmically until it became no more than a black spot in the morning sky.

10

The Sheep Killer

MANY farmers in our area didn't keep sheep because they felt there was too much tending to them for too little in return.

You had to mind them as much as cows and calves, didn't get any milk to sell from them and then when the lambs were sold on, it was only for a fraction of the price people would receive for calves, heifers or bullocks.

My father though was a great believer in 'mixed' farming – that way, he said, a few bob was coming in at different times of the year to "keep the show on the road" as he put it.

For instance he would sell lambs in the spring time of the year, then the sheep's wool in the summer after they were shorn and later on the cattle would be sold and the pigs could be sold as soon as they were ready early, middle or late on in the year.

His biggest reason for keeping the sheep was the way they "cleaned the pastures" for the other animals. For instance you never had a ragwort (or buachalán as we called the noxious yellow weeds) where the sheep were grazing. They could eat these plants without adverse affect whereas they would kill cattle if they allowed them into their digestive system.

Despite all that, I must admit there were times when I agreed with the other farmers about sheep being more trouble than they were worth. The day's shearing was tough on all our backs as we hauled the flock up one by one to the man with the cutting razor; then there was the day we had to bring them to a neighbour's farm for 'dipping' in some sort of disinfectant, the smell of which is still in my nostrils to this day.

That was supposed to stop the ewes and hoggets (female lambs kept on for breeding purposes for the following year) from getting maggots in the hot months of summer and autumn when the Blow Flies laid eggs in nests of dirt around their tailends.

Of course the theory was always different to the practice. On occasions sheep would suffer diarrhoea and consequently became very susceptible to those wriggling nests turning into hundreds of creamy maggots feeding off their hide and their flesh as they literally ate the animal to death.

Just like a young boy or girl with a fever or 'flu, those maggoty sheep became disinterested and lethargic about their grazing and often lay away from the rest of the flock.

At other times they were very visible as they violently shook their tails and even tried to bite around at their own rear ends in an attempt to dislodge the parasites on their body.

Of all the farm chores, removing the maggots was arguably the dirtiest; but we had to front up with my father to do it.

It involved rounding up all the sheep in the field with the dog acting as the enforcer behind us as we tightened them up into a secure corner where they couldn't escape to the road or an adjoining field.

There was often a touch of Murphy's Law about the attempt to catch the beleaguered animal as my father would lose his grip on the wool and the lamb would run free until the dog turned her back into the corner again.

"A good sheepdog is worth two men in situations like this," my father said as he caught the sheep second time around. He then would take diluted Jeyes Fluid out of his coat pocket, douse on the darkened area of the wool where the maggots were and begin strumming with a limp wrist at the sheep's hide to dislodge the preying heads.

My mother said the very thought of the maggots or the smell of the Jeyes Fluid was enough to turn her stomach – so it was that my father got a severe washing down in the scullery with carbolic soap and hot water before he was allowed to sit at the kitchen table for a meal after such an event.

The lambing or yeaning season was at the beginning of the year and because the field where we kept the sheep was a good distance from the farmhouse, there was always the fear of foxes 'stealing' the new born. We used to paint heavy dollops of archangel tar on the back of the neck and the tail area of a new lamb – the two spots where foxes would bite into to carry their prey away.

Even with such precautions, there were times when the fox won out and it was almost like a family bereavement when my father would come in from the fields to declare that a lamb had been lost in this fashion.

If that was bad though, the real low point was when the ewes were 'worried' by a pack of local hounds made up of dogs from various houses in the locale which seemed to come together for what they saw as nocturnal sport.

Unlike the fox situation, the pack didn't just kill or 'disappear' one lamb; instead they savaged several grown-up ewes, hoggets as well as the newly born, sometimes driving them into drains or rivers where they perished either from mauling or drowning or a combination of both.

One year a farmer on the other side of the hill lost 10 ewes in a night of slaughter by a pack leading to the parish priest at last Mass on the following Sunday to implore people with dogs to tie them up at night.

I was small when that happened, maybe four or five, but was perhaps 11 on the night when a local bachelor wandering the roads to kill an hour or two of time before his bedtime, knocked at our door around 11 o'clock.

That hour was considered late in the countryside for anyone to come knocking at a person's door, so my mother signalled to my father to go and see who was calling.

There stood a slightly eccentric but decent man. "Sorry to disturb you at this time of night," he said, "but there's several dogs chasing your sheep up in the Three Fields as I was walking past. You would need to get up there quickly before any of them get killed."

My father thanked him and within seconds had his wellington boots back on, telling my mother to get the torch out and signalling to my big brother to go as back-up with him.

"Bring the sticks (normally used to drive cattle) from the barrel in the cowhouse," he ordered to my brother, as he took down the shotgun, which had come back into the house now that I was considered old enough not to blow my own brains out, from the top of the kitchen mantelpiece.

I was detailed to mind the house which I felt was beneath me, but once my mother gave me that stare, I knew there was no point in protesting.

The order from her was that someone had to stay at base and she tempered it by saying that I could stay awake until they returned from the field.

They were gone for ages and ages and as the clock struck midnight, my eyes were fighting hard to stay open. I nodded off and in my dreams I thought there was a game of cowboys and indians with shots being fired as men fell off horses.

It was just before one in the morning when they came back in – their faces contorted with anxiety over what they had just witnessed.

"Run up to bed, now, good boy," my mother said gently as she hugged me in my prostrate position on the couch in front of the fire; I was too tired to resist and have no memory of anything else from that night.

I only remember waking up on the following morning to the sound of voices coming from the kitchen. When I went down, I saw that my father and mother had been up and out and were now having their breakfast.

"What happened?" I asked. "Were any killed?"

My father put down his cup and looked out the window into the distance.

"It was a good job that man called," he said "or we might have been wiped out. As it was, there are two badly savaged and by the look of them this morning I don't think they will make it."

"Whose dogs were they, Daddy, did you see?" I enquired.

"Half a dozen dogs from the town but the leader was our own whelp. Would you believe that?"

Shep forever sat on the mat outside our back door during the day waiting to go to help bring in the cows or round up the sheep with Daddy. I looked out the back door and saw he wasn't there.

I looked at my father, this time only asking questions with my eyes.

He too answered only with his eyes which seemed to be burning up in that few second stare between us.

11

The Hermit

IT would be virtually impossible for people of my parents generation to understand the amount of travelling we do today as a matter of course on an annual basis.

Just like a life before the internet and instant communication, there was a time when the amount of telephones in any town could be counted on one hand.

In the same way, cars were a rarity and people depended on either walking or cycling to most places. The world they lived in was a small place of a few miles in those days and invariably those who did travel to America or such far-off places seldom if ever returned. It was almost the opposite to the present time where the facility of travel has made the world a global village with people going to and coming from Australia and America commonplace.

For instance, my children were journeying on planes when they were infants, I was in my twenties before I left the country while my father in his 70 years on earth only left Ireland once – on a pilgrimage to Lourdes with members of the local church which was part of a diocesan organised event.

Even journeys inside the country from Dublin to Galway or Kerry to Dublin or Donegal to Belfast or Dublin are now daily events for business people. Once upon a time they were annual events due to distances involved.

I knew several people who seldom left their own turf – a two or three mile journey to their nearest town would be made at most once a week to Mass, while going beyond to the nearest big town would happen at most once in a decade.

The Hermit, an old man I knew who lived on a small holding down in the middle of the bog, was the sole remaining member of a large family, most of whom had emigrated to America by the time they had left their teenage years or early twenties.

The Hermit lived on a farm with a few cows, 15 or 20 cattle and was self-sufficient in vegetables and fruit from his own garden and orchard while he cut enough turf to be able to sell on some and make a few extra pounds.

Even in his early to mid-sixties when I would have come to know him first, he was fortunate that he had another source of income – dollars from America. Not only would his brothers and sisters send him home money but also tobacco and clothes. It was not uncommon to see him in chequered Yankee-looking clothes on Sundays and if you called into his thatched cottage, there was invariably a smell of tobacco which had a much different scent from its smoke than the Velvet Plug or Murray's Warrior my father bought in the local shop.

My uncle was brought up in the bigger holding alongside The Hermit and was like a nephew to him. He had married my aunt and moved up to the high road a mile out of the bog but any day he was down herding or working on his own farm, he would always make it his business to stop the tractor and check on his old neighbour.

The Hermit was seldom in his house; he might be up the bog, or shooting rabbits or talking to one of the cattle he was worried wasn't thriving. Or maybe he was trying to pare one of his asses' hooves which were inclined to grow upwards in front because they were seldom pounding on a surface harder than a bog underfooting.

Life must have been lonely for The Hermit yet he always smiled welcomingly when he saw us coming across his fields.

My parents and uncle and aunt had immense affection for him and would often remember encounters from down the years with him which made them laugh. My uncle who was reared beside him, could have done a PhD on every aspect of The Hermit's life and would regale us with stories of how their hunting for rabbits often became the funniest of memories for him.

He explained that The Hermit wasn't the best shot in the world and aware of this himself, was never content to pull the trigger from distance. Instead, he would whisper to my uncle to sneak up with him a further 10 or 20 yards near the unsuspecting animal. Then as he took aim and was totally focused on his quarry, my uncle would raise his arms behind The Hermit's back and begin waving. The rabbits would see the sudden movement of my uncle and scarper for the refuge of their burrows.

The Hermit, seeing that they were getting away, would rise up onto his feet and charge after them, shooting in scattergun fashion as he ran. Then suffused with anger, he would curse and swear as he performed little riverdance standing-jumps as part of his frustration. My uncle had a major problem at such moments – how to hide from The Hermit the belly laughter that was eating him up inside.

I loved my uncle's sense of humour – his was the original kind of deadpan. I remember my cousin and myself were dispatched to The Hermit's for milk one day when we were on the bog cutting turf. There was a jinx on drumming up in the wild with my aunt's family as every day they seemed to forget something. If it wasn't milk, it was sugar, or butter or sometimes even the loose tea we took out of its packet and put into two sheets of newspaper for transport in the 'Bog Box' with us.

My cousin and I made the most of our courier work. When we arrived at The Hermit's, he was in the yard and brought us inside to make tea. Although we were both only 10 at the time, The Hermit's excitement was not so much in seeing us but stemmed from the arrival from America that morning of a big parcel containing coffee, a shirt and tie, money (I presume this as he didn't mention it specifically) and a new twist tobacco in its own blue pouch.

He took down one of the many crooked pipes he had on his mantelpiece, filled it up, lit it and invited both of us to take a turn pulling on it.

How could you refuse such a moment of forbidden fruit?

My cousin went first and puffed up a plume as if he was a steam engine going uphill. He then wiped the shank and handed it across to me. I tried to do the same but some of the smoke seemed to choke my breathing and I ended up spluttering like a dying motor as I handed it back to The Hermit.

To be truthful I lost my sense of time and space for a while as my head was swimming and when we began to walk back across to our bog, my legs were unsteady under me as if I was slightly drunk. My cousin carried the bottle of milk The Hermit had given us and was busy giving me an official line to tell our parents as to why we took so long.

We could see the smoke from the makeshift fire as we ran the route back in the hope of making up some time but he still had to be at his best as my aunt's face clearly showed she was unhappy that we had taken so long.

He was brilliant in his narrative to her: "He was nowhere to be seen when we called and then by the time he had finished scratching the cow in the hollow field where we found him, half an hour was gone. Then we had to listen to him talking about his parcel from America" – at which point he gave me a big wink.

He had thrown a hook for his mother and she bit on it.

"Well, what did he get home this time?" she asked as her tone changed from annoyance to interest.

By the time my cousin had elaborated and embellished what The Hermit had told us, she was more than happy to forgive us the long delay as she put out the cups and made the tea from the boiling kettle.

We were all called in to eat – we waited while both mothers dished out bread and tomato or bread and corned beef and cups of tea with milk and sugar to wash down our food. My aunt had a great way of letting you know she was enjoying something. "That cup of tea would rise your heart," she said as she sipped it contentedly and sat back to eat her picnic lunch.

My uncle had a glint in his eyes as he watched her. After a while she noticed him looking at her and said: "What are you up to now?"

"Ah, nothing really," he said as he downed a big slurp before putting his cup down between his knees to stop it from spilling over.

"Did you ever see The Hermit milk a cow, Mam," he asked his wife.

"No," she answered. "Why?"

He chuckled: "Well the first thing he does is he spits several times in both hands to soften the cow's spins (teats) and then while he's milking her all that lovely spittle dribbled down into the bucket." As he spoke, my uncle mimed how The Hermit would do it.

My aunt's stomach immediately turned at the thought and she dry-wretched several times. She then got up and walked away without as much as looking at her cup of tea again.

My uncle smiled, took another big drink out of his cup and joked: "Aye for sure, there's ate-in' and drinkin' in that tea."

My aunt refused to talk to him for a few hours after that and it was only when we were having the four o'clock break in the afternoon that we all came together again. She was out of her Gold Flake cigarettes and had to ask him for one of his Woodbines, thereby breaking the ice.

"That was a terrible stroke you pulled on me," she said. "I'm not the better of it yet."

"You're lucky," he said. "I could have told you that The Hermit cleans out the dung in the cowhouse with his hands and a bucket – and that's before he starts to spit for the milking."

My aunt ran off again at the thought of what my uncle was saying – and he giggled as if he was a comedian who had received a standing ovation at one of his jokes.

My mother, who also loved his sense of humour, pretended to get cross with him and told him: "Enough is enough about The Hermit for one day."

Some months later when my aunt and uncle were in our kitchen with Mammy and Daddy after last Mass on a Sunday, they were talking about everything and anything that had local currency – theirs was always, a wide agenda.

The price of cattle, how the milk cheques had changed farming as they knew it, the upcoming TB test were all discussed before my interest was hooked by chat about The Hermit and a sister who, seemingly, was coming back to live in the bog.

As I listened, I ascertained that The Hermit's sister hadn't gone to America but had married into a farm the other side of the county. She was now widowed and not having been blessed with children, was coming back to the homestead to be company for her brother.

That was great news, they all said, because it meant The Hermit would not be alone in his declining years. Almost immediately though there were difficulties as when they went to see the state of the old house, the surveyor's report said it was ready to fall down and suggested that the occupiers leave the dwelling straight away for safety reasons.

His sister had some money from the sale of her farm and agreed to build a new house, but she wanted it closer to the road while The Hermit wanted it to go up on the existing site.

In the end a very small dwelling was erected with a kitchen and two bedrooms and a bathroom on the new site which was over beside the road into my uncle's old farm.

There was a neighbours' welcome home for the sister on the first day they moved into the house and it seemed like a bit of "America at home" as the siblings from abroad also contributed to the new comparative luxury at the head of the road.

Neighbours and relatives from around called and initially it looked like the brother and sister were happy in their new surroundings. As the weather got worse and the autumn evenings turned into bleak winter nights, the sister became more and more lonely in her abode. The Hermit had largely abandoned the house and was forever over in the old yard, only coming in to eat or sleep at night.

I used to feel sorry for his sister as she poured her heart out to my cousin and I about how sad it was that her brother wouldn't converse with her and was shunning her as if she wasn't there.

I never found out what happened but in retrospect, my reasoning is that here was a man who had lived virtually all of his adult life alone. Now in the autumn of his life he was being asked to become a social animal at the click of his fingers.

It wasn't fair, really, and the result was predictable enough. The Hermit knew only one way of life and he reverted to it – talking to the animals, enjoying the company he knew best – his own.

He could, as we knew from experience, dip in and out of social activity when someone called in to see him, but that was for a finite amount of time and then he could readjust to his own ways again.

His sister on the other hand craved for human inter-action, often making my cousin and I stay on to keep her company long after the time that we felt we should have said our good-byes and made our way on to do other chores.

We were surprised when we presented ourselves back home that my aunt didn't give out to us for being late. "The poor woman has nobody and sees nobody, ye were great to stay with her," she said gently, which was in contrast to how she had been cross the time we delayed when getting the milk off The Hermit.

I'm not sure how many winters his sister spent in that state of crying to us about the hardness of heart of a man who would not talk to her. In truth, she ended up being a bit of a broken record to us but following my aunt's explanation of her loneliness, we never once failed to go in when passing.

After my mother died, I was sent away to boarding school and one holiday when I returned I was saddened to hear that The Hermit's sister had passed away.

From what my cousin said, The Hermit had found her dead in the bed on the Saturday, had laid her out himself and waited until first Mass the following day to approach the priest to tell him.

From my cousin's tone, I could tell he was unhappy that even in death The Hermit had not shown a little more compassion. As we went down to the bog past the house one late afternoon, there was no visible life. We had to fodder the cattle and bring some hay home from a reek we had closed off in my uncle's old farmyard so that it was dusk by the time we closed the gate behind us and headed up the road.

As we came up to the turn, we noticed a light in the kitchen of the new house. Stop or not – that was our choice.

My cousin looked into my eyes and drove on. It wasn't being vindictive; just a case of showing respect for the old lady who we felt would be delighted for once that the tractor had not pulled up outside her front door.

12

The Kicking Cow

NATURE chooses and sometimes man loses.

For a few years our cows had mostly bull calves. The implications became apparent after three or four years. We had no young heifer cows of home grown stock coming into our small herd.

That forced my father do so something he seldom had done over the years. He went to the mart and bought a big strong roan cow.

While bulls were worth more in the hand because you would get extra in the sales for them than heifers, my father had a long-term approach.

So if one of the good milkers gave birth to a female or heifer calf, he would earmark those as likely to live out their life on our farm as animals which contributed with a calf a year to our economy and full buckets of milk, particularly in the summer.

This, I hasten to add, was before the time of yields and lactations – that would have been a foreign language to the farmers of that time.

Instinctively my father knew if the cow he milked by hand was giving him quality milk rich in butterfat or a more blue-ish variety which we fed to the calves instead of putting into the creamery milk churn.

In the Ireland of today, it is hard to imagine how the arrival of a cow into our yard caused such a stir. But it did. From the moment the man my father contracted to deliver the new cow out to our house – a seven-mile journey – to the leading of her in from the road outside, a crowd gathered around.

For a start she was the tallest cow any of those there said they had ever seen, erect head with an eye that seemed to survey all around her.

Most importantly though, she had what we called in our neck of the wood "a great bag", that is her four teats or spins as we called them were part of a good milking udder.

That evening at the milking my uncle and three other men came into the cowhouse to watch my father milk her. We had one bucket which held exactly four gallons of milk and she more than three-quarters filled it.

The men agreed that with the transporting to and from the mart and times away from feeding, she would undoubtedly go on to fill the bucket once she settled in to grazing in the fields and had regular milking times.

I can still remember that we bought her on a Thursday, the first milking was that evening and then the world shook on its axis. Not the following morning but on the Saturday morning when my father and the four gallon bucket both landed out in the middle of the yard, courtesy of a double kick from the new arrival.

Around horses or cattle my father was fearless but for the first time in my 10 years on earth I saw fear in his eyes that morning.

"She's not just a kicker but a dirty one at that," he told my mother over breakfast.

Despite the warning, we decided that maybe something had startled her and she was given the benefit of the doubt. The evening milking though proved without doubt that she was a mean machine.

My mother came down for that milking and to help my father she scratched the new cow's hip in the hope that it might soothe her and also deter her from a further outbreak of violence. Half way through the milking the double kick happened again – the whip of her right hind leg first took the bucket out like a ten pin bowler. It was the follow-up kick – which not only kicked upwards but outwards as well, that despatched my father from the cowhouse on his back as my mother too was forced into falling backwards into the shore.

Consternation!

Now we had to bring in the extended family because this new cow was a serious negative on the amount of milk being lost to the churn, while she was a close and present danger to my father's continuing in a state of reasonable health.

For the following milk periods, we had at least two other men around her as my father and the battered four-gallon bucket went in to battle once again.

I watched the new cow's right eye as she took in what was going on around her. When the men were present, it looked as if she would allow the full milking go without incident. Then just as we thought we might get through successfully, she would pounce with those two lightning kicks that had us all back to square one.

My uncle arrived one night with a state-of-the-art anti-kicking jack which was yoked up to the front of her kicking leg and across her hip to the other side for stability. The contraption was supposed to stop even the most wilful of animals from being able to kick by almost paralysing movement.

Not this beauty though. As if she understood what was happening, she merely buckleapt slightly into the air and took bucket and man out from a higher trajectory than usual, albeit with more kicking restriction than when no contraption had been applied.

Theories abounded as to why she was such a filthy kicker. My father's view was that there is an odd rogue in nature which can't be cured. He further hypothesised that the cow had been drugged by the seller so that she could be touched and felt around the mart for milking without reaction. He confided that he had paid over the odds for her because he felt she would nearly fill a churn a day in the summer and would – with the size of her – provide great offspring for the herd.

That plan was now changed and the family were stressed out wondering what was to be done next? Well, we couldn't just sell her on to some other poor unsuspecting farmer and have him killed. My father said he couldn't live with his conscience if he did something like that.

The bottom line was we had to suck up our losses.

He was a resourceful man in these situations and the following evening we milked all the cows except the kicker. Then he opened the calf-shed door and let three big strong red whiteheads in to the cowshed.

They were his trump card. Two attacked her from either side and one started his sucking from the back. She lashed out violently on either side and momentarily cowed the two suckers there. But the young Muhammad Ali in the back had found a way past her guard. She couldn't kick him as effectively where he was and the other two soon copped on and followed suit.

They pucked her violently using their big heads with the happiness that sucking brings. Up and down she was pucked as if she was a small vessel on a sea swell.

Pretty soon, the place was back to normal. And when that trio of calves were ready to move on, we had three more at the ready to put manners on her.

We never did give her a chance to kick a bucket in anger again but we did keep her for years and she provided my father with many fine calves.

For some reason though, he never did allow any of them to become part of our dairy herd – I think he'd had enough of that.

13

Birth Rites

A FARM is a unique microcosm where you meet life's triumph and tragedies as an ordinary day can bloom petals of great joy or equally can wither into an occasion of communal sadness.

From the time I was four or five, I can remember being exposed to births and deaths on a scale that a non-farming young boy could never hope to witness or experience in a full lifetime.

Taking the lead from our parents and uncles and aunts, all the children were hugely empathetic with the animals and their welfare.

Their deaths were treated a bit like a real death in the family – I can remember my aunt crying for hours after the sow had escaped from her pen and killed two lambs with two quick mouth snaps. When we asked her was she crying because of the money she would lose on the lambs, she shook her head: "I should have minded them better and that's why I'm upset," she said.

I recall one time a fully-grown pig died in our sty and my father brought him up to our back door to have him ready for burial down in one of the fields later in the day when yard chores were completed.

When a neighbour, who worked in a shop, came in to deliver our weekly messages, he blessed himself at the sight, offered condolences to my mother, who, while not crying at the loss, was in a state of shock at the way death had come calling to our door.

It was engrained in you to feel those losses – as my aunt said, the money was one thing but it was the sense of not doing your duty or failing to diagnose an illness in its early days that would haunt the adults when an animal was found dead.

The generation who reared us were very superstitious in how they viewed the knock of ill-fortune at their door.

There was always a Job's comforter, who when they saw a cow die or something similar, would forewarn that "these things come in threes".

The funny thing is that there was more than a grain of truth in such claims – I remember one year when we lost lamb after lamb in various ways – foxes taking two, joint–ill (a disease which locked up their movement etc) and for no apparent reason other than they became sickly and didn't recover.

Holy water, prayers after the Rosary, everything was tried to save their hides. I don't remember any supernatural intervention – my father, although holy, was pragmatic enough to know that it was the human intervention, particularly if done in time, which was the most important in keeping the farm animals healthy.

Veterinary surgeons (vets) were frowned on in our house – and a good many others – because, as my father said, if you called them two or three times for the one sick animal, that was the price of the beast gone into the vet's pocket even if the animal managed to recover its health.

Of course those same vets were also to be feared because the Government's numerous attempts to rid the cattle herds of the country of tuberculosis and later brucellosis, meant he (I don't remember a female vet at that time) had the last say on whether an animal was deemed to pass the test or become a reactor.

In one test – I think it was for the TB – the vet gave the animals an injection in the neck area and then revisited the farm a week or so later to check for reactions. If there was a hard lump on one of the animals, it meant it was 'down' and was immediately taken away while the farm was shut down – meaning the farmer could not sell on any other beasts until it was given the all clear in subsequent tests.

My father had his own way of keeping ahead of such an inconvenience. Out herding, he was able to get near the heifers or bullocks which normally would not be as domesticated as the cows or the calves around the yard. He spent hours walking among them in the fields the day before the vet was due to return to do his lumps inspection. By talking to them he was able to get up close to them which enabled him to observe the neck area.

Once he came into the house worried that a big roan bullock about 11 hundredweight and which he had planned to sell within the week had a lump and would go 'down' in the test.

A call for action.

The evening before the return inspection, we rounded up a number of the bullocks in that field and funnelled them into our cattle crush. By then my mother had arrived as instructed with a sweet-can of boiling water in her hand. My father got my uncle to hold the bullock by the nose in the cattle crush as he transferred the water into a hipflask. He then stuck the spout with the near-boiling water to the area where the lump was projecting.

Like a poultice, it drew whatever was inside, so that when the vet probed the area with his fingers the following day, there was a smooth feel to the hide and no lump to alert him that he had a reactor to contend with.

Life was a constant battle of outwitting or being outwitted, not just by the authorities but by nature. You had to 'herd' the cattle or sheep every day –not just to count heads but to examine quarters, urine etc as red in the wee was a sign that cattle could die very quickly.

So much could and did happen but there were balances to be found at the other, more happy, end of the spectrum too.

The year we lost all the lambs felt like no one was allowed laugh or have fun in the house. It never manifested itself as edicts or instructions, more the overhanging sense that life was challenging us with uphill tasks – and there was no time to take things lightly.

Which is why I kept a diary for every cow, heifer and ewe – compiling dates of when they were due to give birth. Perhaps I was a good news junkie but I loved to get up early or maybe go back to a field before dusk when an animal was expecting just to see if they had delivered. If they had and you were the first to announce the news, you could change the mood of everybody. You got a feeling that you had contributed something valuable to the farm.

My brother was in competition with me on this duty as he too loved to find a new calf or lamb. In fact, he had one up on me as once when he and my father were down in the fields, they came across a heifer lying down and in agony as her calf was in the breech position.

Allied to my father's distaste of summoning a vet was the fact that he had a huge amount of knowledge about what to do himself in such situations. Indeed, he was an alternative vet to many of the men on small holdings who would seek his counsel and his help if a cow or a ewe was sick.

In this instance, he claimed that his hands were too large to get inside the heifer's back area and my brother (seemingly) had brilliantly followed his instructions to turn the unborn calf in the passage ways, allowing it to be pulled out more easily and without fear of damaging mother or baby.

He became something of a legend for this great feat so I knew I was up against a gold medal calf deliverer if I ever wanted to get my own bit of glory.

The year started well for me with the sheep. My brother was away in boarding school and I had the run of the lambing season to myself. Even so, there was a huge sense of anti-climax if, as often happened, I came upon a ewe yeaning and she produced only one lamb. The least you would hope for were twins. That year I was present when one of the older ewes presented us with triplets. Having three lambs in one go was a headline maker among the farm folk. It was news out of the ordinary. Our relations and the neighbours would get off their bikes or stop their tractors to ask how the three lambs were doing.

Before the season was out we had three sets of triplets and a real feelgood factor returned to the house. Nature was restoring the balance even if it had taken a few years.

When my brother arrived home for Easter for his holidays, I felt I had him on the backfoot. It was like having a good hand in poker which made you giddy because you felt unbeatable.

Sometimes, though, life has a way of bringing you back to earth very quickly. The mare was pregnant at that time and perhaps because my father said that almost no one ever saw a foal being born, (because it happens so quickly), I became complacent about keeping an eye on her.

You could have knocked me down with a wisp of hay when one evening I came home from my cousins' house to find the house buzzing.

When I enquired off my mother why everyone was so happy, she pointed to my brother: "He's just back from Bentleys (the name on our most remote field) where he saw Molly (the mare) giving birth to Nancy."

A new foal, delivered and christened without me. My full house of lambs was well and truly beaten in that card game. This was a royal flush and all I could do was suck up the fact that I had been trumped in the birth stakes.

The final game came in high summer – August 15th, Our Lady's Day – to be exact.

We had 12 cows at the time or maybe it was more accurate to say eleven and a half cows.

One had broken a back leg as a young heifer and should have been sold on to the local butcher. But she never had any meat on her and besides she proved to be in-calf, thanks to a scrub bull my father ran surreptitiously on the farm.

It was the law that bulls should only be kept if they were purebred but once my father found a young bull-calf which had good definition and lineage through his parents, he was inclined to spare him castration until such time as he knew it would be dangerous not to – which was many months later than the young pretender's peers would have felt the pinch.

We called the injured cow Bachadi (probably because bacach means limp in the Irish language). Limp or no limp she had to walk a mile and a half each morning to our land in Woodfield and a return home often meant 'encouraging' her with a hazel stick to make sure she kept up with the rest.

She was of the Shorthorn breed with a very easy-going disposition but unfortunately she wouldn't fill more than two eggcups with milk on the best of days.

Basically, she was a poor economic resource in the modest milking herd we already had at the time. However my mother insisted that she had suffered enough with her disability and should not be dried up from milking and sold off as a stripper (a cow not in calf and allowed to go dry as a milker).

By this time Bachadi had had maybe four or five calves and because they were half Shorthorn heifers, they weren't exactly premium births.

Normally, my father would try to plan a visit to the bull or a call from the AI man so that the cows would gain the boost of the summer grass. Having them give birth in March or April was a way of maximising the milking potential.

Bachadi didn't even feature on the radar and my father thought that she hadn't come in heat. We certainly didn't think she was about to calve that August because while she had filled out as she got older, she wasn't physically rotund as some cows become when close to going into labour.

We were in the hayfield that day – this was a late meadow we had cut – and as the men were tidying up the last rows into cocks, my father suggested that I should go ahead, round up the cows in the Three Fields and head them for home. His plan was that this would save time and the men would catch up with me after finishing the hay.

I found the other 11 cows in the front field and was a bit miffed that it was Bachadi who was holding up the show. She was nowhere to be seen in the Shed Field which was the second field. That really cheesed me off as I knew now I had to search the back field which was the furthest one from the road. This bit of land was surrounded by double-ditches on one side and as I looked around, I finally saw her lying down at the entry to one of those ditches at the very extremity of the land.

When I got down to where she was, I could see a set of feet protruding from her rear; she was in the process of giving birth. From the blood in the immediate vicinity on the grass, I could see that she already had been working hard at the delivery herself and when I arrived she stood up.

I rolled up my shirt sleeves, aware from countless retellings of how great my brother had been in this situation and began speaking soothingly to her as I had heard my father do many times to other cows in similar positions. I slowly dropped to my knees to examine her pins – the bones on either side of her tail. I knew from having it drummed into me that when trying to help a cow by pulling the legs, the movement should always be downward.

As I pulled in that fashion, I could feel the body of the calf begin to come out of Bachadi without any great resistance. Obviously feeling the relief of movement, she pushed with me and suddenly the calf slipped out enclosed in a bubble of membrane of liquid full of hot water-like substance.

The cow then began lowing contentedly while rhythmically licking the wet hide of her baby with her rough tongue. Within minutes and with a little help from me, the calf stood on infirm legs and tried to get his first suck.

Bachadi turned her head to watch her baby and after a number of minutes she seemed content that the calf had been able to suck in the beestings which came through the teats. It would be a few days before that yellow liquid would be replaced by the milk coming through which could be used by humans at that stage.

I was a bit perplexed when without notice, she walked off towards the river leaving the little calf helpless on his unsteady legs as he and I watched her walk away.

I was caught mentally in the dilemma of minding the calf and calling the mother to get her back again when she went into a clump of bushes tangential to the double ditch and running parallel to the field.

To my great surprise, a second bull calf, slightly more assured on its feet emerged from the thicket and following the intuition of its DNA, headed to its mothers udder area. Bachadi licked its tail and slowly directed her first born of the twins back to where the most recent arrival was. He watched his older brother in action and snuggled up to the teats on the other side.

It was the first time in my lifetime that we had twin calves born on our farm. I watched the two babies bend their backs and enjoy their first joint feeding exercise.

The mother, a former write-off of a milking cow now had her own claim to fame. Twins. It would be an evening of untrammeled joy in our household.

I couldn't wait to see my brother's face.

14

The
Hawk

LIVING on the land is not exactly a jungle but you often come across conflict that is savage for man and beast.

I've seen two rams fighting head-on to near death. That is what they are programmed to do because there can be only one male head of the flock.

Arguably the most brutal attack I ever saw around the farm occurred in the air while we were having a tea break in the bog.

A starling was busily ferrying food to the nest all day, chirping and communicating as it used what places were overturned to find worms and other sources of food for the hungry chicks.

We had followed her progress all morning and early

afternoon and were aware of her continuing toil as we huddled down around the makeshift fire to begin our repast of sorts. Suddenly there was a shriek in the air and a sense of terror was palpable as my father extended his right arm for us to follow the place of attack.

The hawk swooped with an assassin's intent; like a firejet he descended from his hovering position, grabbed his prey in his talons. Within seconds, feathers from the starling flew everywhere as the killer ripped his quarry apart as he flew away.

We were indeed witness to fatal conflict in the air; death in the afternoon and delivered with the sang froid of a professional .

As we drank our tea and chewed into our sandwiches, a pervading sense of guilt descended on us as if we had stood idly by and allowed one of God's innocent creatures to perish before our very eyes.

With the onset of rain almost immediately afterwards, there was a sense of pathetic fallacy surrounding the occasion. As we sheltered under the safe broad branches of a nearby bog sycamore tree, we passed the time looking out at the downpour by recalling the terror one animal or bird can put a lesser types of its species through.

The talk spread across nature's spectrum as my mother pointed to the way lionesses had to hide cubs from their fathers in case they were eaten by them.

"Life is a jungle for animals – everyday there are the hunters and the hunted – in the seas, on land and in the air, as we've just seen," she said with a very resigned tone.

By this time my father had given up on resuming work

and was lighting his pipe, having worked diligently while the rest of us were speaking at cleaning out the bowl and then repacking it with fresh tobacco.

"What about the human jungle?" he asked as he exhaled after one of his first big pulls. "Sure no animal would ever cut up its own brother and feed him to the pigs like happened around here."

I didn't know it then but he was referring to a celebrated murder case which had occurred about four miles from our house in the 1940s when Bernard Kirwan killed his younger brother, Larry, chopped him up to feed his pigs and tried to burn parts of his body.

He also buried the rest of his torso in the bog – but a search by the Guards and helpers unearthed that vital piece of evidence within a short period of time.

It is also well known that the playwright Brendan Behan, who was in jail at the same time as Kirwan, based his play "The Quare Fella" on our near (enough) neighbour.

As my father began to talk about this most clinical and brutal of murders, it was the first time myself or my brother had ever heard of this drama.

In the Ireland of subsistence during 'The Emergency' when there was only the odd radio, a weekly local newspaper and a daily incursion of the Dublin papers, rumour and fact were hard to keep apart.

People 'rambled' – went from their own house to a neighbour's for tea and chat – at night and once the fratricide in Rahan had come into the public domain, it dominated local conversation from morn til night.

I became engrossed in the story – brother against

THE LIE OF THE LAND

brother and then the whole follow-up where Kirwan went to the gallows without ever once admitting that he had done the vile deed – he was put to death on circumstantial evidence.

Thinking back on that day in the bog now, I detect that regardless of the fact that this was a horrendous thing to do, my father had a sneaking regard for Kirwan's mental fortitude and the way he 'played' cat and mouse with the police throughout the whole episode.

"Kirwan was always a bit of a lad," began my father. "I knew him from the fairs and though I never had anything much to do with him one way or the other, he would always nod and say 'hello' when I met him coming or going on the road.

"His brother was the more diligent around the farm. By all accounts Bernie, though older, had little mind for work. He served time for holding up a postman and taking money and they say that when he came back, Larry had no intention of feeding, clothing and housing him when it became obvious his jailbird brother wasn't going to do any work.

"He was the original lazy robber if ever there was one. According to the workman there at the time, Larry took to locking the food away and keeping the money hidden so that his older brother couldn't get near it.

"Locals over that part of the country would say that Bernie began to harbour a growing hatred of his brother and found it hard to accept that he had the power to say when he could or couldn't eat or get a few bob from the farm to go to the pub.

"Anyway, to cut a long and winding story down to size,

they say that Bernie took advantage of the hired hand's day off to kill his brother, cut his head, arms and legs off and feed them to the pigs and bury the rest of the body in the bog. By the time the man – John Foran was his name – went to work the next morning there was no sign of Larry.

"Bernie told him he had gone off to a relation's farm in Kildare and wouldn't be back for a while. In the interim, he was in charge and he sent John in to Clara to buy messages – including whiskey – as part of his day's work.

"It didn't take long for the finger of suspicion to start pointing in Bernie's direction as the hired hand, neighbours and the Guards clearly saw holes in Bernie's story. I think they found Larry's wallet empty the first time they searched the house and Larry also had a car which was still parked outside... it didn't make sense to go to Kildare and leave a car at your doorstep, did it?" asked my father as he spat sideways into the ditch to signal the ending of his tobacco smoking.

"From then on seemingly, the Guards were all over the farm and Bernie like the proverbial cheap suit. There was the occasion after a particularly gruelling session when the Guards thought they had broken him. They had left the house and were making their way down the lane to the roadway when he called out to them to return.

"They rushed back to him.

"'Make sure you close the front gate properly this time because you left it half open last night and livestock could have got out on the road,'" he chided.

"That was the sort of character he was – he had no fear

and in fact could put the fear of God in someone just by looking in a certain way at them. A man from the town was said to have witnessed the murder. He fixed clocks and watches for people and it was sometimes his custom if he needed money to deliver the repaired clock out to a house. It is said that as he shuffled up the lane to the Kirwan house, he witnessed the brutal slaying.

"He came back into the town and didn't speak to anyone in the pub all day. The following day John Foran arrived at his door saying Bernie had sent him for the clock. That put the fear of God into him alright for it confirmed that Kirwan had seen him around the farm and was sending him a coded message that if he talked, he would have his own clock fixed, if you know what I mean.

The poor man was demented with worry and took the boat to England and wasn't seen or heard of until well after the trial had produced a guilty verdict and a hanging outcome. It was then safe for the poor man to come home, though in fairness to him, he never once spoke of what he had or hadn't seen on that fateful day – despite several promptings from locals in the pub over the years.

"The trial itself was eagerly awaited and every day newspapers were snapped up as the defence made sensational claims that Bernie had boiled part of his brother's body and buried the rest. Sure you couldn't make it up. And all the while Kirwan brazenly faced down his accusers, telling them that he had nothing to do with it.

"Yet the overwhelming evidence was that he had

killed his brother and tried to dispose of the body. The jury after hearing the story unfold for 16 days brought back a verdict of guilty on June 2, 1943 – and there are those around who still have a hidden admiration for the way Kirwan defied everyone – except the hangman.

"Still, what he did to his brother was extraordinarily barbaric.

"What you saw there today with the hawk pulling that mother starling to pieces is nature – the law of the jungle.

"What happened in that farm beyond them hills over there defied the laws of God and man and nature for that matter," he said, before repeating the sentence again.

15

The Curse

MADE matches, or arranged marriages as they became better known, were a dime a dozen in the rural Ireland of the last century.

I should know, I am descended from at least three of them. My father was 48 when he married my mother who was 11 years his junior as she walked up the aisle.

As I explained before, his delay in entering the marriage stakes stemmed from the fact that he was the eldest of seven children when his own father died; he ended up being a proxy 'husband' to his own mother, who was a mere 20 years older than him.

She was madly in love as an 18-year-old but her parents turned her head away from the fella she was "great with" and she ended up marrying my grandfather at 19, probably with something of a heavy heart.

I know from my aunts though that she came to truly love her husband and they were a real good partnership until one day the horse he was riding shied at seeing a rat cross the road and his fall ultimately led to his death. So the young and initially unhappy wife became an unhappy widow at the loss of her husband for the remaining 45 years of her life.

She was my paternal granny who happened to be best friends with my maternal granny. It was out of that friendship, with a little help from all sides that my father and mother becoming an item slowly evolved.

It should be pointed out that my mother's mother had long since passed away before any knots were tied or indeed the idea of my parents going out together had taken firm hold.

I wonder if she had been alive would she have given such a pact her blessing, considering how she had been 'stung' in a similar situation with her husband – my maternal grandfather – some 30 years before.

My grandfather was one of a number of brothers who lived together about four or five miles from where my Granny's farm was located. I'm not sure how but she was identified by two of my grandad's brothers as someone who would be suitable for him as a life partner if only.... they could get him to give up the drink.

By all accounts from an early age my grandfather had been struck with this weakness and had little future on his own family farm because of the way he behaved.

The two brothers, who I would like to think were

acting out of a sense of altruism and good nature rather than economic strategy, decided that the only way such a match could be made was if the two of them jointly watched him morning, noon and night so that he not only went on the wagon but stayed on it.

It involved accompanying him to confessions, Mass, devotions and whatever social event – from football to tug-o-war contests – so that he could not buy a drink.

From what my aunt – his daughter, would later tell me – my grandfather was not a lazy drunk and was happy that he was being helped out of the vicious drinking cycle into which his life had descended.

After a number of months on the dry, the two brothers made discreet inquiries around the Delahunty family – my grandmother's people – and an introductory meeting was arranged.

My granny was quite a striking woman to look at while I'm told my grandfather was small, bald and red-faced, yet very winsome in his manner. He was a good storyteller and invariably his accounts of events elevated him in the minds of the listener.

Within the required period of months, an engagement was announced and they were subsequently married, again once it was deemed acceptable in terms of proper delays. He duly moved in to my granny's four-roomed house – a kitchen, a parlour cum bedroom, a dairy/larder and a big kitchen which dominated the dwelling.

Part of her 'dowry' was that she brought a sister to the marriage – she already lived in the house, had her rights to stay there for her lifetime as the second sister and that situation was accepted by all three parties in the unwritten agreement.

Having a man of the house was a novelty to the two sisters who enjoyed his company and the fact that he could direct the workmen on the farm instead of the duty falling on them – as had been the case since their own father died prematurely.

The family's main income had for decades come from owning bulls which serviced the cows of the area. At the time, it was considered slightly embarrassing for a woman to be present when such acts of animal copulation were being carried out in the name of farm commerce. My grandfather's presence obviated that problem and indeed improved the traffic to the bull as men who had eschewed visits by giving their business elsewhere, were now happy to attend with their in-heat animals.

My mother was the first born to my grandparents – as it turned out she was the eldest of three daughters.

However, it was while my granny was expecting my mother, her world fell apart. My grandfather had some cattle for sale and headed off on a Friday morning to the local fair. He didn't return that day, or the next, or the next.

It meant that the expectant mother and her sister had to re-acquaint themselves with doing the outside chores such as feeding, milking and letting the bull in from the bullpark when a cow was brought for servicing.

All the while they kept the secret to themselves that the man of the house had gone missing because of the shame it involved.

About a week after setting out, an unkempt, foul-smelling, drunken man finally returned home late one night slurring his words and swaying under the influence. My granny had no choice but to vacate their bedroom as they nursed him slowly back to sobriety.

That wasn't easy – it involved her sister and herself stealing down the back roads to the town, tapping on Molloy's private house adjoining the shop and confiding to the lady of the manor what their problem was.

She told them their secret was safe with her and to her eternal credit no word ever passed her lips about how the sisters needed to buy a dozen bottles of stout and a naggin of whiskey every second day for a further week to wean my grandfather out of the stupor he invariably landed himself in once he went to a fair.

In all the talks I had with my aunt about her father's problems, she never once mentioned that he was violent in drink. However she did emphasise that once he came out of the drunken state, he would be very cross about the money that had been spent and would beat himself and everyone else up about it in a verbal sense.

My mother could remember the fear – not of violence – but the weight of shame that had a layer of fear stitched into it, every time he left the house to do what on the face of it was legitimate business.

She was exposed to the quiet nudge and wink of my granny and her aunt trying to bring him back to normality and the unhappiness in the house while those dark days slowly passed.

By the time the next child was born some four years later, the women of the house had adapted their lives to what was an inevitable cycle. They had formed an alliance of sorts – probably a suspicion of everything about my grandfather being based on a false premise, just like the introduction to the marriage itself.

As a sensitive man and maybe because of rather than despite all his problems, he was aware that his misdemeanours were a source of great shame on the two adult women. It was also heartbreaking for him that my mother would recoil at any advances he would make to lift her up or hug her or sit her on his lap from an early age.

And so it was that my aunt, the second born, became his overwhelming favourite because she always ran to him no matter what state he was in. By the time my last aunt on that side of the family was born some three years later, the middle girl was exerting increasing influence on her dad's behaviour.

Prompted cleverly by her mother and aunt, and indeed I'm sure by my mother with whom she was inseparable in life, she would ask her daddy from under her golden curls in a determined way not to drink at the next fair.

Probably taken aback by the sheer innocence and maturity of the request, he managed to comply; it was a matter of great jubilation when he returned on the evening of the fair without "darkening the door of a public house."

My aunt covered his face with kisses and indeed the other women lightened their mood for the first time since the inaugural outbreak had taken place. There was light in the darkness that had invaded their lives.

He was dead by the time my aunt was nine years old

– from drink. But it is testament to the personal hell he went through in trying to avoid alcohol that all the women had by the time of his passing, an enormous regard for the lengths he went to stay sober – and the way he treated them when not in the jaws of his obsession.

Every day the demons followed him around and every day my aunt accompanied him and banished them by being his little girl every step of the way.

My mother loved learning and was sent to boarding school by her mother so that she could become a teacher. That plan changed following her father's early death and instead she went to work for the rest of her single days in the town's post office.

My aunt was every bit as bright but from an early stage it was ordained that she would become the farmer in a house full of women– and every day she milked cows and fed calves with her daddy just so that the status quo could remain in the household.

Inevitably, my grandfather for all his determined efforts to avoid meeting his nemesis in a bottle, would occasionally find a temptation too much if he bumped into a neighbour or old friend down the town or after Mass who liked a jar. Then when he would return and finally get weaned once again back into the real world, he would be overcome with a sense of guilt that he had let the woman down, and particularly my aunt, his pride and joy, with his behaviour.

"Sometimes it was like I was watching a magnet drawing him," she told me. "I watched him shaking as his inner demons demanded he run from the fields and hasten to the town to satisfy his habit.

"Once when he ran into the house, put on his clothes and was half into his top coat as he made for the road... I ran ahead of him, sat down in the middle of the road and began to cry. It stopped him in his tracks that time – but we all knew it would not work the next occasion he was possessed," she said with a tear in her eye at the sad recall some three score years later.

"I loved my daddy and I tried every way I could to keep him from falling. The day he died I cried the most bitter tears and I swore a drop of alcohol would never cross my lips."

The woman lived until her mid-eighties and was as good as her word. Her father's drinking lifestyle was the motivation for that and the way his end came was both tragic and sad.

He was only in his mid-forties when one evening he departed this world from his sick bed as she was feeding the cattle up in the Hill Field. During her walk back home, she saw him in the Pump Field hurrying diagonally towards the railway line – something she felt was odd particularly as he was sprinting across the field like someone running for his life.

She thought it decidedly odd since he was a weakling lying on his death bed half an hour earlier when she set out to do her chores.

It was only when she arrived at the gate into the house that she saw a candle lit in the kitchen and the other women on their knees crying and saying an impromptu Rosary for the safe delivery of his soul into heaven that it dawned on her that what she saw might not have been real.

In retrospect she believed that what she saw was his spirit departing across the fields he had come to love and tend to in the married years he had been the man about the place.

The shadow of my grandfather and the great family weakness percolated all the way down into the youth of both our families. My mother, as she grew up in childhood, came to love him, faults and all and like my aunt, would try to be a motivational factor in his fight to the grave against the demon.

She said life was tough enough without any other generation descended from him having to endure what he and they went through. Near her own death prematurely from cancer – she got both my brother and myself to swear we would abstain from alcohol for all our adult lives.

"I don't want some poor unsuspecting person like my mother to have to put up with what she had to go through," she said.

Through tears at our own impending loss of her loving presence in our house, we both made her that solemn promise.

My aunt said afterwards that my mother had died happy because of that talk with us.

It was easy to stick to that promise, knowing how a good family man had lost his battle to be a great husband and father because of the hold alcohol had over him.

16

Black And Tanned

MY grandmother on my father's side was widely regarded as the kindest and wisest woman of her time.

But the toughest shower of mean-spirited louts ever to enforce law in Ireland (The Black and Tans) were to see a different side of this soft-spoken young mother – and walk away stunned.

You have to be 'of' the land to truly understand why.

As we saw in John B Keane's 'The Field', people have been driven all the way to kill for something they have tended to with their hands all their lives.

The earth of a farm gets under a man's and sometimes a woman's skin and enters their soul. It can lead to serious fallings-out with those around you and more tragically, to family feuds which have been part of the landscape ever since time began.

As they used to say, where there's a will, there's a row and when there wasn't a will, there was an even bigger one.

The poet Patrick Kavanagh's depiction of the hunger for land in his poem 'Epic' contains the following quote: 'Who owns that half a rood of rock, a no-man's land. Surrounded by our pitchfork-armed claims, I heard the Duffys shouting, damn your soul?'

It might only have been rock but it was the Duffy's rock and you could go to hell if you tried to take it off them.

Granny bred the opposite into my father, his brothers and sisters with the notion that while land helped pay the bills, you couldn't bring it with you in the coffin. Therefore if someone was losing their reason about a perch or two of land, it wasn't worth falling out for generations over, she would argue.

While that is of course a noble view of the precious earth in designated field areas, it wasn't pragmatic especially when it came to dividing up farms from fathers or uncles down to the next generation. Greed has its own set of morals.

Fortunately my Granny was spared that sort of headache, otherwise she might have had a different view of the value of the smallest piece of field.

As it turned out, two of my father's brothers died young before they had met women to go out on their own and look for something either on or out of the farm. The two others were as different as chalk and cheese; the elder was a mechanical genius and worked in the mechanic's room in the factory of our town which employed 1,200 people in its jute mills at the height of its powers.

He helped out on the farm when he wasn't working there while my father's youngest brother stayed on the farm until he met his future wife. It was then incumbent on my father as my Granny's eldest and in the absence of a father who had died tragically, to offer help to his brother to buy a farm. They finally found one in Kildare which they could afford, some 35-40 miles away from our homestead.

One of my father's sisters went to work in the Sweepstake in Dublin and became independent from an early age, albeit living with an aunt of hers in Leeson St. The younger sister, the baby of the family, was born six months before her father died and grew up seeing her oldest brother as a de facto father in virtually every way.

When she got married – on the same day as my father in a double wedding as it transpired – my father was only too delighted, in conjunction with his mother obviously, to give her a house and land, which a cousin of his who had died childless, had bequeathed to him.

That meant that by the time we came along all of the family had been looked after except my uncle, the mechanic. In the interim years, he had been sacked in the factory for throwing a spanner at his boss, who was a neighbour and milk customer of ours.

He then began a sawmill in the yard alongside the pigs, calves, cows, hens etc and showed his expertise in carpentry as well as motor mechanics. The only problem he encountered was that he had the world's worst business acumen and unless a person paid him, he would never send a bill for his services or material.

That forced him to try his hand at work in Dublin where he effortlessly added the skills of plumbing and roofing to his already wide work portfolio. As a consequence of his array of skills, he was never idle a day until he retired – unless he took a week's holiday to come 'home' as he always called it.

He was lucky in that the woman he met had a good business head and he was able to keep on top of his invoices so that a steady stream of money came in to help pay for their house and the four children which they had in their family.

Yet while he wasn't in love with the land in the same intimate way as my father was after walking and working every blade of its grass all his life, my uncle had his own deep relationship with every field which made up our holding.

The land may have been a wife to my father; it was more of a mistress to my uncle. You could tell he had a passion for it by his recall of what happened in different fields during his growing up days.

He was particularly nostalgic the night his mother died. He talked about how hard she had worked as a young widow to bring up seven children. He was 10 when his father passed away, four years younger than my dad and it was left to the two of them – my father as sergeant and my uncle as lieutenant to run the show with my Granny doing what she could outside while minding and feeding the other five children.

He died around the time the Black and Tans arrived

in Ireland. The responsibility fell on my father and his little brother, to bring the cows one and a half miles up and down to our land in the morning and the evening. They faced daily danger from the curfew introduced by the Tans. This meant every one had to be indoors by a certain time with the same restriction on movement applying before dawn.

There was also plenty of Republican activity going on around that time and the Tans had a very simple rule of thumb – if the 'Oirish' caused them any trouble, they would return it in bucketfuls.

When the IRA blew up the Woodfield bridge which serviced our fields along the main artery to the next big town, the 'Tans put a temporary bridge in situ for their own convenience but refused to allow any of the 'natives' through. It meant that, as in our case, if you wanted to move cows, you had to do a two-three miles detour to get them over to the other side.

Such walking on cows would leave them with precious little time to graze with the result there would be a huge drop in the volume of milk they could supply. And as we delivered milk to customers around the town, it could have a big impact on the money my Granny could call on to buy groceries and farm stuff.

She was a resourceful woman and decided that the two lads were better off milking the cows in a field which could only be negotiated by travelling down a long lane. That offered them an element of safety in her mind.

That part of the farm she normally kept for fresh grazing in the latter part of the year but on this particular year because of the circumstances they faced, she felt it was a better option to open it up earlier in the season.

She knew the type the 'Tans were, made up in the main of ex-servicemen who had responded to ads in the British press asking them if they were ready to "face a rough and dangerous task". The adverts drew a huge response not out of national pride but because they were guaranteed to get paid ten shillings a day.

Many Black and Tan units all but terrorised local communities. They worked to a very rudimentary set of rules, one of which my uncle claimed was, "if the order to put 'hands up' is not obeyed straightaway, the Irish could be shot without recourse to any other warnings."

They also kept it simple for themselves as to who did or did not deserve to get caught. The old adage – if in doubt, take them (the Irish) out – was popular as they genuinely believed they would, in large part, be killing rebels anyway.

The animation in my uncle's demeanour and the anger in his voice was still tangible half a century later as he told my brother and I how himself and my dad got through that time of fear.

Their mother had them forewarned that no matter what the Black and Tans might say or do to them, they should never react and always be courteous and respectful.

That came a little easier to my father than my uncle. Following a number of weeks in which they had to suck up having their bucket or churn of milk 'accidentally' spilt during the Tans' inspection of what was in the pony and cart, my uncle was close to breaking point, though he knew it would be foolish, as he was not big enough, strong enough or armed enough to take on the battalion stationed beside our land.

The leader was a particularly anti-Irish bloke who thought nothing of roughing up what was in effect two boys in front of him. It got to the point where the lads decided that they would do the morning milking before dawn and come home through the fields. Granny was worried about their welfare but having gone for one week without being able to supply milk to neighbours, she knew that something different had to be done.

They had a wheelbarrow to carry the churn and buckets in and under her supervision worked out a route which kept them hidden along ditches well away from the roadway.

One morning as they did their usual check from the beech trees down in the field where the cows were being kept, they saw in the gathering of the dawn a strange movement some distance away in one of their fields.

In the half-light they could make out a figure doing sprints up and down the field – this leader obviously believed in keeping fit.

The boys looked on in fascination as the leader of the 'Tans used the back field of our Three Fields to run up and down along the side. Then after about 15-20 minutes, he stopped, took off his clothes and jumped into the river to cool down. When he came out he used a flannel to dry himself down.

However, instead of putting his clothes back on at this point, the Tan started marching exaggeratedly up and down the field, turning and presenting (sic) as the moment inspired.

He was in the middle of one of these movements when my uncle roared out "halt" at the top of his young voice; the Tan immediately covered up his privates and leapt into the protection of the ditch where he dressed hurriedly into his uniform, all the while scouring the horizon to see if he could detect who had been watching him.

My father felt like killing his brother for what he did, telling him prophetically that they (The Black and Tans) would not rest until they got revenge.

The two boys swiftly made for home across their own little beaten track and could hear from the activity along the river that the troops were already out looking for them. When they got home with the milk and had it strained and ready for delivery in the town, my father told his mother what had happened and what to expect.

That night as he loitered in conversation between houses with a man in later life my uncle would try to behead in the factory with a 9-inch wrench, a bullet was fired in their direction which scudded past my father's feet and ricocheted off the end wall.

An hour later when it was well past the curfew time, a loud knock at our front door was answered by my father who was immediately confronted by four Black and Tans. By the time my Granny appeared out from the kitchen at the back, they had my father in 'cuffs and were escorting him over to the barracks.

She threw herself between my father and the man who was leading him with a revolver stuck in his back.

"Leave the boy alone," she demanded. "He's 15 years old. You can take me in his place."

That flummoxed their plan somewhat. Despite their known cruelty and distaste for diplomacy, the fact that they were dealing with a woman complicated matters for them.

"He's well able to shout abuse at me when it suits," the leader retorted.

"That was me," said my granny. "How dare you use one of my fields to run around in the nude. I have a good mind to write to your King and tell him what's happening in his name. We can never set foot in that land again without thinking of how you and your country defiled our land."

The leader's eyes were fixed on her and his face went from mirroring thunder to one which became pale and almost fearful as my Granny let his colleagues know she was prepared to make a big case out of his nude walkabout.

"Let him go," he ordered the Tan who had put on the handcuffs.

They did as they were instructed.

My father was saved in that way from at least a brutal beating or possibly worse and thereafter my Granny arranged it that every time the cows had to be milked she was there with the boys.

My uncle, who had told me this story, got up as he ended his tale and walked across to where his mother was waking in the bed.

"What a woman," he said looking down at her in awe.

He shook his head and said with a half-smile on his face and a half-tear in his eye: "Hard to believe that saint of a woman lying there was the first Irish person to put the wind up the Black and Tans."

And then he laughed: "But she was right, you know. I've never walked into that field since without thinking of the 'Naked Tan'".

17

The Fair Day

TOWN met country one day a month in the summer time when the local Fair Day was held as I was growing up; it was the nearest thing to razzmatazz which rolled our way.

Buyers with cheap crinkled brown suits stuffed into green Wellingtons to protect the lower leg from the liquid dung the day manufactured. A 'Cheap John' shouting at the top of his voice from his strategic position in front of the Post Office. "Roll up, roll up, get your special bars of rock and exotic cola only at this stall."

Later he would introduce 'Kiss Me Quick' hats to the front of his counter and hold a box of wrenches on display, telling the farmers: "all your fixing needs in one

THE LIE OF THE LAND

small box and I'm selling it for a knock-down seven and six (7/6).

For the day, the shopkeepers seemed to take their cue from him with paper posters on their front windows offering "special deals".

Every area of the main street had its demarcation lines – the calves were up towards the green, the bullocks and heifers were bang in the middle of the street and the sheep and pigs were further down towards River St.

All human life – and me and my cousin – was there.

The big treat was to get the day off school if your father was bringing cattle and he needed help to mind them through the day.

That only happened once in a very blue moon so normally we had to be content with seeing Cheap John, the Jobbers with the cattle and the calves with the white scour on our way home from school.

Only once was I allowed to take the day off school – a Friday – to be part of my father's requirements for the Fair Day. At the previous fair in another town, my mother and I had arranged to meet him as he was to accompany us to the big drapery shop to buy my First Holy Communion suit.

He was glad to see us as he had endured a tough day before selling off the cattle he had brought. He didn't like to keep stock that didn't look well or were slow to thrive. These were such a bunch and he was glad to be rid of them, regardless of what price he had to settle for.

What became an even harder chore was buying the suit; the poor shop assistant must have taken down 20 different makes and colour and still my mother didn't like any of them.

We ended up agreeing on a greenish suit with white flecks which my mother described "as the best of a bad lot."

We then went to a nearby cafe and had ham sandwiches and tea and by the time we were ready to head for home, we all felt much better again.

As we were walking down the street, a man in a lorry waved to my father and then pulled in to the side, his brakes making an air-splitting screeching noise. He was a Jobber who doffed his hat to my mother in deference before beginning his pitch for a sale to my father.

"How the idle rich live," he said merrily. "In town buying new clothes and the rest of us struggling to keep an arse in our trousers."

He let out a big laugh again, all the time eyeing my mother to ensure his language wasn't too coarse on her ears to be offensive.

I looked up at her and she was smiling and enjoying his effort at good humour.

My father was a step ahead of him. "That's what's called a softening up line," he explained to my mother. "These Jobber lads are past masters at it and before you know it, they'll have sold you a calf or weanling that can't put four feet under itself because it is so weak."

The Jobber slapped his knee as a growling laughter came from deep within his nicotine-filled chest right through to the hairs at the end of his nostrils.

He was showing he could laugh at both his own and others humour – all in the line of farm commerce.

He pointed to us to go around to the back of his lorry where he slid back an opening on the back door which allowed you to look inside.

"The last animal left in the Fair today and you'll have nothing only luck if you buy her."

My father tried to head him off at the pass by explaining that whatever few bob he made selling earlier was well and truly dinted with my new Holy Communion suit.

On the mere mention of 'Communion' the man stuck his hand into his pocket and thrust a "half-dollar", as he called the old two and sixpence, into my grateful hand.

My mother told him that was "way out of order in terms of generosity."

That done, the Jobber looked at my father with an eyebrow raised and said: "Take a look at that heifer now and I'll tell you there'll be plenty of half-dollars to be made the day you go to sell her."

I would say my father had no intention of getting involved in a haggle over price because he was genuinely not interested in bringing home a beast which appeared lopsided.

My mother mouthed at him to show some sort of civility.

"I can't even see it properly through that little hole. Open up the back and let me take a good look at her," he commanded.

The man did what was asked of him, all the while talking to my mother. "I'm telling you now, Mam, as sure as eggs are eggs, this one will turn a nice few bob for ye in no time at all."

In the half-light of the truck, the heifer looked to be a very dark roan about 18 months old but thin at the rear and bloated, as I suspected, on one side.

"With very little that heifer could be turned into something special," claimed the Jobber.

"Aye," said my father, his eyes dancing with mischief. "You're right there. Very little and she could turn into a corpse."

At the time stock like this one, if in good shape, were selling for £20 a head. The man asked for "an even score" which drew a big gasp from my father.

"Go on, then, go on. Make me an offer?"

They talked and harangued each other without my father showing any great interest.

Then after several minutes, he said: "Right, I'll give you a tenner and that's it."

"Ah, mother of the divine, you'd pay that for a calf never mind a heifer nearly ready to breed," he said with what I felt was only a mock-feeling of hurt in his voice.

My mother was holding my hand and gave it a little squeeze before she interrupted. "I'm not trying to influence the outcome of this great duel," she declared with a chuckle in her voice, "but we need to be going down to the hackney man for a lift home now – and I don't think he'll bring a heifer in the back either."

What should have been a big drawback to the Jobber turned into a glorious opportunity. "You'll have to fork out a nice bit for that lift but sure once we complete the bit of business here, I'll deliver the heifer and your good selves to your own front door."

"What are we going to do so?" asked my mother, looking over towards my father.

"Divide it," I heard myself say.

"Divide it," repeated the man. "You heard the goson. Divide it."

He put out his big right hand, spat in it and held it towards my father.

"Are we going to deal or not?"

"Fifteen pounds is a handful of money for a beast that mightn't be alive in the morning," said my father, who nevertheless encouraged the proceeding with the remark: "There had better be a good luck penny with her."

The Jobber snorted in air through his nose with a great sense that the kill was about to be made.

"As the man above is my witness, but you are the greatest robber I've ever dealt with," he roared, knowing the apparent slander was in fact a compliment, endorsing my father's true worth as a buying adversary.

"Fifteen quid and five bob of a luck penny and I can tell you truly that it's losing money I am on this one – but sure I might win the next time our paths cross. And the main thing is we haven't broken the young lad's word here," he added as he tossed my hair with an approving hand.

My mother was delighted to get into the cab of the lorry out of the evening chill. She smoked a cigarette, something she rarely did, on the way home to honour the occasion, as the Jobber put it.

Within half an hour we were home, the new arrival in the shed and my mother had opened the whiskey bottle to 'handsome the deal' with the Jobber and to thank him for the lift.

The man stayed until my father took out his Rosary, at which time the Jobber jumped up, drained the remnants of his glass, saying: "God bless all here" to no one in particular as he made his way to the front door on less than steady legs.

My mother saw him off and then worried that he was not in a fit state to drive. My father assured her that the lorry knew its own way home.

He was slightly giddy in his demeanour and I thought he charged through the Rosary a little quicker than normal.

Sure enough, he was animated in his discussion as he sat down for the tea and hot cake afterwards. "You know we've bought that heifer 'in her sins'," he remarked as my mother asked him what he planned to do with her.

"My plan is to get her ready for the Fair Day here next month and see if we can turn a profit. I think if we look after her well, we can get her ready by then."

I wasn't convinced. "What about the way she is bigger on one side than the other?" I asked.

"I examined her there while I was putting her in the middle shed and I punctured the bloated side with my penknife and she seemed to deflate a bit. If it continues that way, she will be as right as rain in a short time."

The month flew until our own town's Fair Day and every day we fed and watered the heifer as if she was animal royalty. True to the hunch he had on the first night, the animal's lopsidedness disappeared over the first few days and her dark roan colour made her stand out.

On the eve of the Fair Day, my mother told me she was sending me along with my father "for the luck that is between ye with this heifer."

We looked slightly anaemic as a gathering at the fair; we only had one beast while around us there were farmers there with dozens of cattle for sale.

When you were 'working' at the Fair, you were treated well by all around you. My father told a neighbour who was gasping "for a wet" to go into the pub as myself and himself would mind his cattle. When he came out about an hour later, he gave me a bar of chocolate and told my father to bring me in for a treat as he would now look after our solitary beast while we were gone.

The publican was a little man in an old-fashioned grocer's brown coat with a hat who talked funnily and had a way of pricing spirits, beer and minerals at different rates, depending on who was doing the purchasing.

I noticed my father shaking his head in disbelief at his change. He was a pioneer and only appeared in the place on rare occasions; obviously he was paying a higher tariff than the regulars.

By the time we went back out the day had moved on and we were surprised to arrive back at our spot to find none other than the Jobber examining our heifer with the neighbour we left behind to mind her.

Another man, a stranger, was also standing there, asking how much the animal was going for. On seeing my father return the neighbour said: "Well, we have the very man back now to tell you."

My father was a little coy about coming out with a price in front of the Jobber. "Tell me what you're thinking and I'll know then where you stand," he said.

The man walked around the heifer a few times, bent down to have a look at her undercarriage and then went to the head to examine her full on.

He stroked the stubble on his chin several times as if in deep thought but didn't fall for my father's trap of getting him to show his hand first.

The cat and mouse game was underway and it took an immediate twist when the Jobber entered the equation.

'If that man is not interested in buying, sir" he said in my father's direction as if he was a total stranger, "then I'll bid you twenty two pound ten for her."

His voice was authorative and persuasive as if what he was saying was 100 per cent genuine.

The other man continued to examine the heifer from all sides. Finally, the stranger spoke to my father. "I will give you one offer and one offer only," he said with an emphasis on the word only .

"I will give you twenty five quid for the heifer, but you'll need to give me a good luck penny to go with that."

I could tell my father was pleased but true to his nature, he put on a poker face and made it look as if he was contemplating the offer.

As he hummed and hawed, the Jobber spoke up.

"A fair price makes a fair deal. And that's what we have here. A fair animal. A fair price and now a fair deal. You won't break my word. Shake on it there and there's two happy men going from this day's fair. There'll be plenty of half-dollars to be made on both sides," he stressed, as he winked surreptitiously at my father.

"I won't break your word," said my father, as he stuck out his hand to the man.

The man shook it back and the deal was done. The Jobber said in his view a deal wasn't a deal until those involved had a drink to seal it.

He pointed over towards the pub. My father nodded – he understood the ritual that would be played out.

18

The Banshee

MY parents and their ancestors were devout Catholics and most of our neighbours were the same. Even the Protestants families we knew were devout in their own religious devotion too.

They were respected all the more for that, even if they wouldn't be saved unless they somehow managed to 'turn' miraculously on their deathbeds.

Growing up in the sixties, there is no doubt that the church dominated our lives.

As well as regular confessions and Mass, there were nightly rosaries, weekly novenas, holy hours, devotions, benedictions. These were all topped off with the lenten campaigns of devoutness, the month of the Holy Souls in November while not forgetting the missions and the legendary missionary preachers threatening hell and damnation as well.

All of these were woven deeply into the texture of our way of life – and these were only the overt pieces of our religion. The less conspicuous parts were the beliefs – every bit as genuinely held onto as the orthodox stuff – which had nothing to do with the church.

For instance my mother's side of the family had a total integration of pagan rituals into their day to day living.

If a visitor walked into the cowhouse during milking and didn't say: "God bless the work", he or she was immediately told to go out and to re-enter but this time to utter the right words. My mother or my aunt or whoever was milking would then answer back: "And you too."

Similarly if one of them was making butter and someone came in and didn't touch the churn and say "God bless the work" it led to an immediate inquest as to why they hadn't performed this ritual.

My aunt had a deep disdain for red-haired women going near her farm and in particular her dairy, saying she had seen it time and again over the years where their very presence led a baffling reduction in milk volume from the cows or an imperfect quality butter being manufactured following such a visit.

There were different worlds alive in their minds than is the case nowadays.

My father was forever praying – maybe because he talked about supernatural happenings as if they were real.

He was in dread of black dogs – this came about from his encounter with one beside the Protestant Church when he was a youngster coming from his Granny's house back home to ours.

Night had descended and instead of walking through the town, he decided to take a short cut up the Green Road. As he did, he noticed a dog ahead of him and threw a few stones in his direction for the fun of it. The dog turned around and according to my father, "his angry eyes were like saucers.".

That was frightening enough, he added, but then the dog turned and ran into the church grounds through the locked gates.

It was only when my father was walking past the gates he noticed that while there was about six inches between the bars at the top, the bottom halves of both gates had bars about every three inches.

"How could a big dog, with a massive head and body go through such a small space," he reasoned as his legs turned to jelly. He recalled how the dawning of this fact paralysed him as he tried to run as fast as he could in the direction of his own front door.

He also spoke once of coming home from devotions one night and saying 'hello' to a neighbour. She didn't answer and when he looked around two things immediately struck him – the woman had died a number of months previously, something he forgot in the spur of the moment, and she had also disappeared even though there was a high wall behind where he had encountered her... and really there was no place for her to go.

My uncle's stories were less intense than my father's and probably more enjoyable as a result. He lived up past the old Protestant Minister's where there was a hollow sound in the road which was supposed to be from where bodies were buried under some mysterious circumstances.

He recalled hearing footsteps following him home one night to the point that he was afraid to look around but felt the sweat drowning his shirt by the time he turned off the road down his own boreen. He never quite explained what happened in that escapade but he did with two others which, on the face of it, seemed like genuine supernatural experiences.

Once as he passed the graveyard, the sound of bells suddenly shook the still of the night – worse than that, a massive light shone out through the window of the old Abbey ruins at the end of the graveyard.

"I said to myself: If ever I'm going to meet the devil, it will be tonight,'" he told us as we gathered around the fire listening, afraid to look behind us in case some human with horns was standing behind us waiting to pounce.

Transfixed with fear, he decided that instead of rushing down the road he would wait and see what followed. As the seconds passed, the bells sounded again but he also picked up the bleating of the goats who had invaded the old Abbey in search of its ivy which they liked to eat.

While that was happening, the splutter of an engine in the distance was immediately followed by the light leaving the abbey window and swerving onto the road up on a hill from a neighbour's house. He was a truck driver, had obviously left the vehicle running while he went in to get something in his house and remarkably where he had parked was directly in line with the Abbey although he was about a mile away on higher ground. When he drove away the apparent mystery of the light, just like the mystery of the bells until the goats made their noises, was banished.

"After that," my uncle said as he pulled deeply on his Woodbine cigarette, "I said to myself that I'll hardly ever meet anything out at night much worse than myself.'"

The Christian-pagan overlapping of beliefs is, or was perhaps not unexpected, given the background of the Irish people. Throw in the 'fairy' element and the milieu was indeed potent enough to affect virtually every waking moment in an Irish household.

I'm not sure if I ever bought into the whole fairy thing; even to a child's mind, it lacked the gravitas of devils and hell and ghosts that frightened the living daylights out of you just by thinking of them.

The fairies appeared capricious in the way they operated; swopping babies for old men in prams or stealing babies for the sake of it. My mother used to sing a song lamenting such a loss: "Fair thee well my child forever, in this world I'll have no joy, but in the next I ne'er shall sever, there I'll find my baby boy."

They also seemed mischievous as can be instanced by the countless number of people who lost their sense of direction in fields at night. My aunt swore that she knew several farmers who couldn't find the gate in a field they knew like the back of their hand once the fairies began their nocturnal games of disorientation.

Seemingly, there was only one way to get out of such a situation – if you were the poor unfortunate lost soul, you had to sit down in the middle of the field, turn your coat inside out on your body and then when you went looking again, you'd find the gate that up to then had eluded you.

I was 12 years old when the worlds of real and virtual religion coincided in my life.

In the summer time of year, my uncle, the teacher as distinct from those who were farmers, went west with his wife, my aunt and their two children once he got his holidays.

He was gone two weeks and while he was away my father contracted pneumonia and was confined to bed. In a time when very few had home phones – mobiles were several decades down the road – information was either meticulously pre-planned or passed on when people met up.

When my uncle was leaving Galway to come back, he was offered a sheepdog called Darkie – replete with muzzle because he was quite cross. This uncle felt that my dad would like a new dog after what had happened with Shep, our previous mutt, having been put down for leading the killing of our own sheep.

That evening there was consternation around our house as the newly-arrived dog snapped at anyone and everyone who tried to get him out of the boot of my uncle's car.

My mother said: "See if you can bring him in to the

room where he (my dad) is and if he doesn't get on with him, he'll have to either go back to the west or be put down."

It was only when two other uncles arrived as reinforcements that the three men approached the boot to open it and do what my mother had directed. Darkie growled threateningly but the men had armed themselves with two hurls and a yardbrush in case they were attacked. My uncle unlocked his car and lifted up the lead while using the brush to protect any potential lunges by the dog in his direction.

Slowly they negotiated the animal into our downstairs bedroom where my father's friendly greeting of: 'Darkie, here boy' brought about an instant transformation in the dog's demeanour and humour. He jumped up onto the bed alongside my father, wagging his tail and happy to accept that this man was someone he could do business with.

My father took off his muzzle and the dog licked him and seemed totally relaxed and happy in his company. My mother, though was still forced to flee for her life and the sight of any uncle putting his head around the door drew long, gutteral growls.

My father was too weak to get up with his illness which meant that either the dog stayed the night in the bed or my mother did – not both. Around dusk, and in a desperate attempt to find a solution, she opened the front door, sent in the uncles again with their various arms at the ready who succeeded in getting to the bottom of the bed unscathed. Then they whooshed at the dog which finally leapt from the bed to the floor and fled into the dark of the night.

As was her wont, my mother blessed herself in thanksgiving on seeing his black tail with the white tip disappear and declared: "He can go where he likes now but he's not coming back in here."

During all this time my brother and I kept a very low profile – he had a dislike of dogs, particularly those he didn't know well enough to trust while I was worried about the damage those jaws could inflict upon my legs.

Darkie howled on our front window sill through the night and the next morning when I was delivering the milk to our neighbours, one of them asked had I heard the Banshee?

"No." I said. "Where."

She looked at me with a dark stare. "Your house," she said. "Don't you know that the Banshee follows certain families and yours is one of them."

I had slept soundly in the backroom with my brother all night and wasn't aware of the dog's howling antics at that time.

What I remember is that the following morning my brother and I prepared for the milking as was the case since our father was unable to get up. We opened the door in the outside shed to collect the buckets for the handmilking chore which lay ahead.

As we did so, we saw Darkie at the back sitting on the hessian bags we used for the barley when it was harvested later in the year. The blood froze in our veins as we waited for him to attack us. Instead he stood up, stripped his teeth in a smiling rather than threatening gesture and wagged his tail. It was as if he was saying: "Ok, I'm part of this family now, so let's be friends."

We were delighted to have a new dog and it was all the better that he refused to be friendly with anyone other than our immediate family members. Our aunt, who was my mother's sister, often would go down the yard after last Mass on a Sunday to look at the calves and pigs, found it disconcerting as she became the subject of growling and barking from Darkie.

My father came out of his sickness quicker than expected following the arrival of the dog. He told us that when he saw the black dog in the room, he thought he had passed on to the next world; but when the dog came to him rather than away from him and snuggled up in such a friendly way, it gave him a surge of great energy which made him feel better almost straight away.

The opposite happened with my mother. She had been diagnosed with cancer a few years before but had rallied several times so that we thought she was over the worst of it.

She seemed to lose her strength very quickly and by the end of summer was confined to the very same bed my father recuperated in from his pneumonia. During those months when my aunt would come down more and more often to be with her, Darkie became a subject of hate for the two women while my father and my brother and I grew to like him more and more with every passing day.

I felt closer to my mother than anyone else in the world so that when we were working down in the fields and she needed to be minded, I remained behind. After the nurse visited her to give her the injection which soothed her pain, she would rest peacefully. I would often steal in quietly and watch her breathing, touch her wavy hair, and caress the lovely high cheeks which forever kept her skin taut on her face. Her glasses always tilted to the side she was lying, which gave the impression that she had fallen asleep while a little tipsy.

I would then go back out to the kitchen and ask God and Padre Pio to save her because I truly couldn't imagine the house without the sound of her voice.

It filled every room and filled all the chambers of my head – she loved to poke fun and used the oscillation of her tone as the instrument to deliver the message she wanted to get across.

I sat as usual in the kitchen playing sentry the day before she died. In the quiet I dozed off but woke up startled as I heard her talking to someone in the bedroom.

Who, I wondered, had come in while I slept, like the old priest Peter Gilligan, on the chair? All the other relations were out drawing in the hay as were both Daddy and my brother down on the farm. It was a remarkably warm day and earlier she had asked for the outside doors to be left open to create a breeze which would circulate around her bed.

She continued to talk though no other voice answered her back. I thought as I tiptoed to the room that she might be raving a little from the effects of the injection.

I quietly walked in through the open doorway and then it became clear what was going on. She was talking to Darkie, gently massaging his mane and telling him that his job was to mind us when she was gone. His snout leant closer and closer to her; they had made their peace in the end.

She noticed me in the half-light, tilted her head to allow her glasses to sit properly back on the bridge of her nose. She smiled on seeing me as she had always done, put out her hand for me to hold and confided as she glanced at Darkie: "He's come to look after me."

I went back out to the kitchen and stared into the fire as I said bitter prayers – accepting now that they would be ignored from on-high.

My mother died just before midnight and after the priest arrived to anoint her and the family had said a Rosary for the happy repose of her soul, we went our separate ways to bed.

I couldn't sleep with the pain of loss I felt in my heart and the haunting of what I had witnessed with Darkie that afternoon.

I told my brother and my cousin who stayed with us in our double bed the story. The three of us lay side by side looking up at the ceiling, taking turns to talk about her through our tears.

Just before the dark began to banish, we were stuck to the sheets in fright as we heard Darkie howling. He sat on her bedroom window sill all night as if on guard, just like he had done on the first night he arrived from Galway.

Everyone was up early the following morning to go to first Mass.

Our nearest neighbour was out as we were passing and seeing us all dressed up asked my father if everything was alright.

He told her that Mammy had died late the night before.

"Ah that explains it," she said. 'The Banshee was back again. I knew from the first time that it wouldn't be long. God rest her soul."

Acknowledgements

WITHOUT realising it, I had written this series of stories The Lie Of The Land in my head many years ago, but I never got to write them down on paper until this year.

For over 29 years I've had a great partner in my corner, my wife, Rosemary, who has always had one simple piece of advice – write about what you know.

When I told her that I was finally doing this, she became my in-house editor, in tandem with my eldest son, Barry. Their feedback was invaluable and helped me reshape some of the more clumsy bits in the book.

Thanks too to Paul, Ronan, Rachel and Patrick for their observations.

The catalyst for getting me up and running on this project was Gerry Duffy of 'Who Dares Runs' and 'Tick, Tock, Ten' fame.

As it transpired, Gerry's 'better half', Jacinta O'Neill was also a catalyst as by reading each story and offering immense encouragement she made sure I completed what I'd started.

My brother Ed read the stories with his critical eye and said he heard a genuine 'voice' coming through. His green light was important because he is these stories as much as I am. The same can be said of my cousin D (Donal Devery), who also read the book and clarified a number of things which added to what I had written.

I have talked about neighbours and friends who we got on with and also about people who didn't see us as friends. But the stories have been recounted in a way that was true and factual and I hope not offensive to anyone.

Thanks also to my cousin Michael for helping me in getting the message out about the book and to my niece, Emily for having the final say in proofing.

Words are one part of the equation of writing a book – it is how they are then set out and designed that makes the difference. I was lucky to get the most talented layout man in the business – Joe Coyle.

I would also like to thank RTE's Damien O'Reilly, Ana Leddy and Ian Wilson for broadcasting two of the stories – The Rosary and The Kicking Cow – on the Countrywide radio programme on a Saturday morning. The response was very positive and helped me realise there was an audience for such stories.

Lastly to the memory of my mother and father, both of whom were dead by the time I had left my teens. They still walk the earth with me every day. I need them because more than anybody, they did indeed know The Lie Of The Land.